Gargoyles

dead ink

First published in Great Britain in 2021 by Dead Ink,
an imprint of Cinder House Publishing Limited.
ISBN 978-1911585640

Cover design by Luke Bird
lukebird.co.uk

Cover photography by JVPhoto / Alamy
Gargoyles Illustration: George Koutroumanidis
Kevin Picture: Richard Valencia for Goldsmiths' Fair
Picture of author & whippet: Tania Powell
Typeset: Laura Jones

Printed and bound in Great Britain by Clays Ltd, Elcograf, S.p.A.

www.deadinkbooks.com

Gargoyles

Harriet Mercer

dead ink

For my mother,
and sister,
and Alice and Maddy.

In memory of my father.

I who can blink
to break the spell of daylight
and what a sliding screen between worlds
is a blink

Alice Oswald, 'A Rushed Account of the Dew (Falling Awake)'

Chapter One

10 March 2008

Swathes of green and yellow fields fly past, moving without me: I'm running up a descending escalator, going nowhere, with a python coiled round my ribs. I wake up to a stitch tearing at my right side. Peculiarly the tightness eases if I lift my right arm. My phone flashes 3 a.m. Harvey's barking, I get up to let him into the garden. My legs are leaden, and it's as if I'm walking through waves, against the draw of current. Back upstairs, one step at a time; the snake constricts to a surge of nausea. I get my head over the loo just in time and vomit, eyes streaming. The bathroom floor has stretched, the corners have been yanked out; its grey has become the whitest sheet. I crouch down and tip over onto my left side, arm gravitating, and the floor is soothing, compress-cool to my cheek; all invisible footprints are forgotten. *Relax*, I tell myself; the python squirms, as if it will burst out of this drum-tight body. I call out and my voice pinpricks the air. A second attempt rouses my mother. I try to answer her questions; my grunts are enough for her to call an ambulance. There's a moth on a blind slat, her wings flickering. I put this stitch under a microscope, it's colossal: a wisdom tooth abscess was painful, migraines debilitating, but this is different.

The ambulance crew arrives: man and woman. *Is your stomach normally this big? ... Are you pregnant?* It's true, I had been wondering why my tummy hadn't been responding to the thirty-six or so miles I was walking a week, and put it down to the dark chocolate habit. *No, I'm not pregnant.* The snake's strangling: I can't get enough breath. My writhing makes it impossible for them to get a blood pressure reading. I feel panicky and don't want them touching me.

'Not much wrong with you, though your heart's going like the clappers. We'll get you checked over at West Mid. Right, can you stand up for us,' he says without a question mark. My body has seized, it's plank stiff and won't bend; won't obey. They tell me again and again to stand, *There's nothing mechanically wrong with you.* I process their impatience; I cannot even sit up. Again they insist, and now I swear at them in frustration.

'How would you move her down the stairs if she'd broken her leg?' my mother intervenes, her face white and worried.

'We've got a blanket in the ambulance that we use to roll up dead people and bump them down the stairs; we could use that if you like?' comes the answer.

She demands they call another crew with a stretcher. When the second team arrives, they are warned, *She's a very rude girl,* as if I'm a badly behaved child. This crew doesn't carry a stretcher either; they administer morphine and oxygen and pull me to my feet. One each side of me, we somehow get down the stairs. It's cold and rainy outside and the gravelly road scores my bare feet.

'Stay awake Harriet, stay awake!' in the ambulance, their tone different now. But I can't fight sleep.

West Middlesex Hospital. I open my eyes to a circle of faces peering over me; I'm in a cubicle.

'Are you a bit of a drinker, Harriet? When did you last have a drink, Harriet?'

'No. Had some … wine at lunch. Sunday lunch.' I don't know whether they hear me.

'Harriet, are you pregnant?'

Again. *No.* A battery of questions. Is my name dissolving, is that why they keep repeating it? I turn to my side and vomit pale green liquid. No one notices. I watch the bile trickling down the side of the bed, it gains momentum and the drips splash onto the floor.

So sleepy.

Wasp. On my arm. I rub the sting … it's lumpy, plastic. Someone moves my hand away.

'Try not to touch it, Harriet … it needs to stay in.'

It. It. It.

I fight my eyes open, a red tube loops up from inside my left elbow … a long way up to a dark red bag hanging from a stand.

'Harriet, do you want to see your family?' By magic they are at my bedside. I'm puzzled; my sister, Emily, should be asleep in Berkshire. She holds my hand. They're smiling at me. My hair is stroked and I want to tell them not to because it's full of sick.

Alone again with the bluey-green-clad brigade.

'I'm going to give you a catheter, it'll be more comfortable.'

I apologise profusely that I haven't shaved my legs today. Catheter doesn't hurt.

Sleep again.

'Hello?' I call.

'Harriet, keep as still as you can; you're doing really well, it's nearly finished,' answers a male voice over a speaker. I look up and find myself semi-enclosed in a white donut. Sleep.

Somebody leans over me.

Harriet? She speaks urgently. *We have to remove your kidney.* I see an NHS badge pinned to her blues, Jessica Worth Anaesthetist. Thirty-something. Big glasses take up half her face. Sadness fogs her eyes – and fear. *Remove my kidney?* This must be a dream. *Yes. You've got a tumour on your kidney. It's bleeding. It has to come out.* Still the same expression from behind her

3

glasses. The red bag sways above my head like a metronome; I feel my brain examining the word *tumour* in revolving slo-mo. *Am I going to die?* My question seeks a no-nonsense response. She takes my hand. *When you're better, you must come back and visit us.*

Awake. A tall man is talking to Dr Worth.

'You *cannot* risk taking it out. The blood loss is already catastrophic.'

'What other options do we have?' Dr Worth has her hands on her hips; *cannot* is still ricocheting around and around.

'Embolisation. We'll transfer her to Charing Cross. The bleeding has to be stopped.'

'It's far riskier, moving her. Theatre's ready, and ...'

'The ambulance is waiting. Radiology's on standby. She'll have a chance if we get the vessels sealed.'

My bed had started to move before he finished the sentence and now I'm being wheeled down a corridor with more of the bluey-green people. One of them strokes my head. 'We're taking you to Charing Cross Hospital. Your family's following us.'

Let's have a blue light, shall we? says the tall doctor to the ambulance crew. I listen to him and the accompanying medics' chat, *Yeah, Spurs crushed the Hammers ... They got lucky ... Traffic's heavy, isn't it? Rush hour should be over. What time is it? Ten?* It's as if I'm there, but not there. Distant. 'Hello?' I hear myself call from time to time. They don't answer. Perhaps they can't hear me.

There's a blast of chilly air and a window of cloudless blue sky as I'm wheeled from the ambulance into the hospital and we're crammed into a lift.

Tall man disappears, four or five other doctors remain with me, all busy with tubing and bleeping machines; it's as if I'm an extra in some film production.

'Harriet, we need to put a tube in your neck, it might feel a bit odd ... okay?' says one of them, his face close to mine, he squeezes my hand.

The push-pressure of the tube going in is more disconcerting than the cannulas that are put in both arms. I listen to the team become agitated as to why theatre isn't ready. And then, after a while, 'Right Harriet, time to go. Try not to worry; we're going to look after you. You'll feel sleepy now. Take a nice deep breath.'

*

A lovely, warm-sounding woman is speaking on the phone when I open my eyes. She hangs up. I feel fine. A rubbery plastic box is clamped over my face. She leans over me, *You're okay, Harriet. I'll take this mask off in a bit.* Her voice is scented with toast and Earl Grey tea, and sits me on a sumptuously cushioned sofa. As good as her word, she frees me from the breathing box and replaces it with a lighter mask. Sleep again.

Critical Care: Days 1–5

A nurse dips a cotton wool bud in water and moistens my lips. I bite at it, sucking every micro-drop. She laughs, *Oh no, you mustn't do that.*

The clock ahead of me says 9 p.m., and from my bolt upright position I survey my new surroundings on the High Dependency Unit. My eyes gradually become accustomed to the translucent blue hue. Apart from the beds, it doesn't much look like a ward. It's space-age: state-of-the-art monitors next to every patient, bleep-beeping; twinkling away, like firefly car lights in an urban nightscape. Vast easels stand at the foot of each bed where immaculate nurses are meticulously recording vital numbers. I watch the nurses glide rather than walk and note that I'm the only patient to be awake at this moment.

I vomit. A nymph flutters by and assists the nurse pushing a tube up my nose, down my gullet into the stomach. It scrapes my nostrils; I'm spluttering, gagging until I manage to snatch the tube out. Nymph doctor sprays my throat with something to stop the gagging, and then holds my hands down while the nurse threads the tube.

'Sorry,' she says, 'it's horrible, I know. This sickness complicates things with your collapsed lung … the tube will prevent you from vomiting.' I swallow it down on the third attempt.

Nurse does quarter-hourly obs and checks on the wound. Wound? What wound? *Abracadabra* – she peels back the sheet to reveal the top of my right thigh where there is a rectangular dressing.

'Where have *my* legs gone?' I chuckle.

'What do you mean?' she asks, eyes darting. I tell her that these fabulously plump legs spilling over the long white surgical stockings are twice the size of my legs. It doesn't bother me, but she scurries off to the doctors' and nurses' station – a glass-fronted room from where they peer, always in deep discussion.

I close my eyes, and there's a wall: old, crumbling mortar; red bricks pitted with holes, tunnels. Eyeballs. In pairs. Popping out. Bloodshot. With worms. Wriggling. Spiralling. Around pupils. Whirlpool. Fathomless. Gaze. *The wall is birthing faces.* Mucus oozes. Drips. From cracks. Beaked noses, fleshy lips, protruding tongues, they sprout. Sliding out. Faces thrust forth. Telescopic necks. Twisting. *Look away!* I can't. An untouched brick. Its pores. Enlarging. Seeping. And. Another. Face. Is born. How many? A hundred? Goblins. Nope. Gargoyles. Gloating. Spitting. Spewing. Gunk. Fingers. Gnarled. And. Mouth-pulling. Screaming venom. Devil horns. Tongues entwined. Can't.

Open. Eyes. Theirs. Sucking. Swallowing. Mine. And. Thoughts. Memories. Extracting me. From me.

My body jumps, pulling on tubes, as I open my eyes. Heart's pounding. Hot. Recalibrate to blue hue. A doctor passes by, smiling. Fix on creases in bedclothing, waiting for the gargoyles to reappear. *It's okay*. They've gone. For the time being. Every time I close my eyes, they return. Morphing from the wall, freakily hypnotic. That feeling when you've drunk too much and the ceiling's spinning. Only this ceiling is hell's meadow. So I stay awake.

Pillows drift south and east and west. I watch the clock hands. Dali-like they wring out each minute to the distance of a marathon, synchronising with the non-stop bleeping and flickering red lights. I shouldn't be here with these very sick people.

Along with new legs – now encased in inflated pulsating boots – I notice with indifference that the inside of my left arm is bruised black-purple from wrist to elbow. Nothing bothers me. I accept, without question, all that is alien: that I cannot sit up unaided; the tangle of tubes (sixteen, my mother says), the cannulas, neck tube, oxygen mask, catheter; even the male nurse that comes to wash me. The immediate past and future are of no consequence. When, though, on my second morning, two nurses manoeuvre me into the chair next to my bed, I am fuzzily shocked: my stomach is enormous, it looks beyond a full-term pregnancy; and by the realisation that I cannot walk. My new legs are faulty. I try to put one foot in front of the other, they are impossibly heavy and pain sears up my body.

The curtains on this Grand Production of Life go up at 6.30 a.m.; nurses choreograph their assigned patients, checking their notes, medication, washing them, dressing them in fresh hospital gowns, and by 8 a.m. each patient, if conscious, has to be sitting in the chair next to their bed, with as many pillows as it takes to prop them up. They await the entrance of Dr Mark Palazzo, Director of Critical Care.

He enters, surrounded by a buzzing entourage of registrars and doctors. I recognise nymph doctor and several other now familiar faces as they assess each patient. The respect that he commands is palpable. My suspect sense of humour is evidently still intact as I visualise him sashaying down the catwalk in his own branded, wide-legged palazzo pants.

After an hour and a half of being in the chair, it's back to bed. My bed. It's like a waterbed. The mattress ripples beneath me.

A beaming, besuited, NHS-tagged doctor perches next to me. 'We've been up all night talking about you; you're quite a star!' Words escape me as I struggle to assimilate this bizarre statement with my new surroundings. Perhaps sensing my bemusement, he hurries off.

A machine starts bleeping and flashing in time with my accelerating heart. Dr Palazzo is reducing my oxygen dependence and the mask has been replaced with a nasal cannula. I reach out, to grab anything that will return my breath. I'm gasping from a vacuum, a freshly hooked fish, flailing in a bucket. My eyes flit from face to light, to machine, to ceiling, to a pair of eyes, to IV stand, to someone's mouth – it's talking to me but I can't hear what they are saying, I only see the shapes it makes – in a fearful merry-go-round. The breathing battle culminates in the return of the Bi Pap from Recovery, sealed over my face. 'Not many patients can tolerate this,' the registrar says to my family; guilt stabs me as I read the fear that has hijacked their faces. I catch my breath amid the whoosh of the machine; it's sheer relief.

Palazzo dictates that I need to try again with the lesser mask. And then the nasal cannula. A supermodel nurse that could be Naomi Campbell's double sits with me, gently bullying me – actually, not so gently – to regain control of my galloping heart that rests at 138. 'Nice deep breath and count to ten ... and exhale; slowly mind. C'mon, if you can't do this we'll have to ventilate you.' *Like I want to feel like this*, I want to answer back. But I'm grateful for her presence. A portable X-ray machine is wheeled to my bed for a chest X-ray; I think of asthmatics encountering this terrifying breathlessness on a regular basis. I promise that I will never make a fuss over a cold again. I want to go home.

Mr Winkler, consultant urologist, visits. 'Hello Harriet, it's good to see you.' It's the first time that I put a name and face to *the tall man*: shaven head, glasses, intense blue eyes, a real smile. 'If it wasn't for Mr Winkler ...' My mother had left the sentence dangling.

A brief examination, then he pulls up a chair, sits back and locks his fingers together as if he's about to tell me a story:

'So, what you have is this lump on your right kidney, an Angiomyolipoma ... it's a bit of a giant, actually, 30cm ... about the size of a rugby ball.'

'Is it cancerous?' My mother has already told me it isn't. I need to check.

'No. It's a benign tumour.' Small smile. 'But its blood vessels make it ... explosive. They're very inflexible compared to normal vessels, of other tumours. If you get extra blood flow going through them, they "pop". And when that happens, as it did in your case, it's very serious ... But you know, loads of people – mostly women, actually – have them, minute ones, and they'll never know they exist.' He raises his eyebrows in emphasis. 'They become dangerous once they grow over 4cm ... at your size, they're very, very rare, about twenty-five cases worldwide in the past fifty years. We don't know an awful lot about them, not much has been written, unfortunately ... they didn't recognise it at West Mid; I suggested it would be safer to embolise your AML rather than to remove the kidney. Which is why you ended up here.'

'Embolise?'

'Yup. A radiological procedure; my colleague Nick Burfitt put a wire in your groin which travelled up to your right kidney. From there he blasted the rogue vessels. Not as simple as it sounds, it took him over four hours, you were bleeding heavily. He did a good job. You're fortunate to have survived it.' The big smile again.

'Breathing ... difficult.'

'Right, so all that blood you lost is now trapped in the abdominal area, we call it a haematoma. That haematoma is so enormous that it collapsed your right lung ... and it's impinging on nerves, which is why your mobility's affected ... and why your tummy's distended.'

I'm not enjoying the thought of my body ballooning with blood; I envision it being syringed out.

As if reading my mind, 'We can't drain it, too much risk of infection. Your body will reabsorb it eventually.'

'Am I going to die?' My question sounds out of place and my voice unfamiliar.

'The next three weeks will be critical. You're not quite out of the woods yet. There's always the possibility of a re-bleed, and of the blood in your haematoma becoming infected. You'll have to be monitored very carefully. And beyond that, you'll have to think about surrounding yourself with gadgets for the next six months. We have to watch and wait.' Another big smile. Although I absorb all his words, I'm still blurry and protected from their full significance.

My mother and Emily visit every day and stake out the café in the hospital foyer at lunchtime, in the hope they will spot Mr Winkler as he buys his sandwich. As busy as he must be with his numerous other patients, he seeks them out, updates them and offers them reassurance and no doubt gets bombarded by questions. It hurts to see the worry etched on my family's faces that they endeavour to disguise, and to see their expectant smiles as they walk towards my bed when they visit. But this is the only pain that penetrates the drugs, as I lie awake dodging gargoyles.

My gargoyles illustrated by George Koutraminidis.

Chapter Two

Language in Pain
(for pain is a place)

Finally, to hinder the description of illness in literature, there is the poverty of language. English, which can express the thoughts of Hamlet and the tragedy of Lear, has no words for the shiver and the headache.

Virginia Woolf [1]

It was as if those twenty-six letters had been wrenched from the void; my own hoarse voice seemed to emanate from a far-off country.

Jean-Dominique Bauby [2]

While I lay on the bathroom floor with what was later discovered to be a ruptured angiomyolipoma on my kidney, I took time out to analyse the pain that was squeezing my lungs: I remember thinking it possessed the tight ache of a stitch, albeit magnified until it surpassed migraine pain, and the toothache of a root-canal abscess that I'd suffered the year before. It was so consuming that I decided it must be on a par with childbirth. These were the points

---

1   Virginia Woolf, *On Being Ill*, (USA: Paris Press, 2002), p.6

2   Jean-Dominique Bauby, *The Diving-Bell and the Butterfly*, (London: Fourth Estate, 1997), p.49

of reference for my answer of *ten* when asked by the disbelieving paramedic to rate my pain on a scale of zero to ten, where ten was the most extreme. But who knows, my *ten* might have been another person's *five*, or perhaps someone else's *twelve*. Degree of pain is only comparable to that which you've experienced before, and description (whether adjective, metaphor or number) is complicated by subjectivity.

Virginia Woolf decreed malady to be a casualty of language, that there are no words to adequately describe even the everyday headache. Ever since the onset of migraine in childhood, I've had to find words to convey headaches. I remember seven-year-old me being examined by a dour neurologist. More than his demeanour, I'm curious to remember how I described the pain in my head that would have my mother take me by the hand and lead me to my bed – given that adjectives such as stabbing or throbbing probably hadn't had cause to enter my vocabulary. It wasn't until my twenties that the migraines sparkled with their tiara of auras: shimmering raindrops – haloed with white light, and holographic – float across my vision, obliterating faces and text. The auras only last thirty minutes or so, and as alarming as they are, I always remind myself that the attacks are nothing compared to epilepsy. In the opening pages of her memoir *Giving up the Ghost*,[3] Hilary Mantel wonders whether 'a flickering on the stairs', which she has supposed to be her stepfather's ghost, is instead:

> (…) nothing more than the warning of a migraine attack. It's at the left-hand side of my body that visions manifest; it's my left eye that is peeled.[4]

---

3 Hilary Mantel, *Giving Up the Ghost*, (Great Britain: Fourth Estate, 2010)

4 Mantel, *Giving Up the Ghost*, p.2

Migraines are renowned for affecting one side of the head; Mantel reveals the pain in that *peeled* eye. And she gilds her visual disturbances:

> Small objects will vanish from my field of vision, and there will be floating lacunae in the world, each shaped rather like a doughnut with a dazzle of light where the hole should be. Sometimes there are flashes of gold against the wall: darting chevrons, like the wings of small quick angels.[5]

Migraine aura is treated with Gothic gold leaf, and the headache transforms into a fairy-tale baddie:

> … a migrainous sleep steals up on me. It plants on my forehead a clammy ogre's kiss.[6]

Metaphor allows Mantel to express how powerless she is mid-attack. She addresses a further unnerving symptom – of how migraine disturbs language:

> 'Don't worry,' I say, as the ogre sucks me into sleep. 'If the phone wakes, it will ring us.' I knew the migraine was coming yesterday when I stood in a Norfolk fishmonger choosing a treat for the cats. 'No,' I said, 'cod's too expensive just now to feed to fish. Even fish like ours.'[7]

Apart from her peeled left eye, Mantel does not focus on the ache itself, she chooses instead to show the electrical interference.

---

5   Mantel, *Giving Up the Ghost*, p.5

6   Mantel, *Giving Up the Ghost*, p.4

7   Mantel, *Giving Up the Ghost*, p.4

Some might say triumphantly, *Aha! Virginia Woolf is right! Not even Mantel can describe the headache pain.* But the truth is that the pain of migraine is so much more than just the pneumatic drilling on the side of your head; it includes all the neurological short-circuiting, and nausea too.[8]

Pain is the protagonist of many illnesses. And once in the stranglehold of acute pain, the kind that blots out everything else, it is pretty much impossible to articulate its nature. Although I was inwardly dissecting my discomfort when collapsed on the bathroom floor, it's true to say that in the moment of crisis I was unable to verbalise my thoughts. Elaine Scarry echoes Woolf when she writes:

> Physical pain is not only itself resistant to language but also actively destroys language, deconstructing it into the pre-language of cries and groans. To hear those cries is to witness the shattering of language.[9]

But surely it is a temporary resistance and 'shattering'. Alphonse Daudet kept a notebook during the last decade of his life that recorded moments in the latter stages of his syphilis, its symptoms, pains and the treatments he took.[10] He too mourned the inadequacy of words:

> Are words actually any use to describe what pain (or passion, for that matter) really feels like? Words only come when everything

---

8   And tactically, Mantel's concentration on the otherworldly dimension of the headache is of course suited to her memoir's ghost character.

9   Elaine Scarry, *The Body in Pain*, Kindle edition (Oxford University Press, 1985), Loc 3801

10   Daudet intended to write a book about pain; instead, his notes were first published thirty-three years after his death, in 1930.

is over, when things have calmed down. They refer only to memory, and are either powerless or untruthful.[11]

It is interesting that unlike Woolf, he draws attention to the fact that pain is far from being alone in its slipperiness, that actually any abstract entity – whether it be 'passion' or 'the thoughts of Hamlet and the tragedy of Lear' – demands a wrestle with language for expression. A little later, he describes:

The varieties of pain.

Sometimes, on the sole of the foot, an incision, a thin one, hair-thin. Or a penknife stabbing away beneath the big toenail. The torture of the boot. Rats gnawing at the toes with very sharp teeth.[12]

He may well be remembering the pains, and coating his memories with metaphor to articulate them, but his words are hardly 'powerless or untruthful' – for only someone who has experienced nerve pains could conjure and convey images of such specific, exquisite agony. And in the chilled cyber nightclub of metaphor, the readers' imaginations sip, or down in one, another person's imaginative reality; it enables them to slide into Cinderella's slippers, or to recoil from Mantel's ogre kiss, or to scrunch their own toes as they squirm away from the sharp teeth of Daudet's gnawing rats.

In the seventeenth century, the metaphysical poet John Donne likened his life-threatening illness to 'a kingdom' in his narrative *Devotions upon Emergent Occasions, and Several Steps in my Sickness*:

---

11 Alphonse Daudet, *In the Land of Pain*, ed. Julian Barnes, trans. Julian Barnes (Great Britain: Jonathan Cape, 2002), p.15

12 Daudet, *In the Land of Pain*, p.21

The disease hath established a kingdom, an empire in me, and will have certain secrets of state, by which it will proceed and not be bound to declare them.[13]

And when you are first able to gather your bearings in illness, it feels indeed as if you have been parachuted into an alien country without the necessary currency in your pocket, or language to help you integrate into its culture. This is nowhere more evident than in the story of Jean-Dominique Bauby, who quite literally had to rearrange the alphabet in order to communicate from his condition. Bauby, editor of French *Elle*, suffered a brain-stem stroke at the age of forty-three that resulted in locked-in syndrome: he was left mute, a quadriplegic, paralysed save for some movement of his head and the left side of his face, and a patient of Berck-Sur-Mer's Naval Hospital. The impetus for his book, *The Diving-Bell and the Butterfly,* came from monthly letters he began mailing to a list of sixty 'friends and associates' in response to Parisian gossipmongers who denounced the erstwhile editor as 'a complete vegetable'. Bauby set out to prove that his 'IQ was higher than a turnip's'.[14]

The alphabet was shuffled to aid his means of communication:

'E S A R I N T U L O M D P C F B V H G J Q Z Y X K W'
The jumbled appearance of my chorus line stems not from chance but from cunning calculation. More than an alphabet it

---

13   John Donne, *Devotions upon Emergent Occasions and Death'd Duel* (USA: Vintage, 1999) p.59. Donne's 'kingdom' undoubtedly feathered Susan Sontag's opening of what she later referred to as her 'polemic against metaphors of illness' (*Aids and its Metaphors*): '(…)Everyone who is born holds dual citizenship, in the kingdom of the well and in the kingdom of the sick …'

14   Bauby, *The Diving-Bell and the Butterfly*, p.90

is a hit parade in which each letter is placed according to the frequency of its use in French language.[15]

The code was devised by his 'Guardian Angel' speech therapist, without it he would have been 'cut off from the world'.[16] Visitors read through the letters until Bauby blinked his left eye; they repeated the process until a word and then a sentence was formed. This was how he dictated his letters, and indeed the book[17] ('written' in just eight weeks, July–August 1996, six months after his stroke). The effort required to complete his memoir was herculean: he would 'churn over every sentence ten times, delete a word, add an adjective, and learn my text by heart, paragraph by paragraph'; blinking his left eye was 'the equivalent of weightlifting' when compared to his daughter's effortless cartwheels along the beach.[18]

We read *The Diving-Bell and the Butterfly* at book club. Laura, a sociology lecturer who has had cancer, ignited the discussion with her assumption that *at least he was never in much pain*. It was a view that baffled other members of the group, and with much animation we set about citing excerpts we perceived to be full of pain, an example being the page-long chapter, 'My Lucky Day':[19]

For half an hour the alarm that regulates my feeding tube has been beeping out into the void. I cannot imagine anything so inane or nerve-wracking as this piercing beep pecking away at

15 Bauby, *The Diving-Bell and the Butterfly*, p.27

16 Bauby, *The Diving-Bell and the Butterfly*, p.47

17 The strategy is known as partner-assisted scanning.

18 Bauby, *The Diving-Bell and the Butterfly*, p.80

19 I'm not sure that Bauby's vignettes are strictly chapters, as only a couple are as long as a conventional chapter, but for reasons of clarity that is how I shall refer to them.

my brain. To make matters worse, my sweat has unglued the
tape that keeps my right eyelid closed, and the stuck-together
eyelashes are tickling my pupil unbearably. To crown it all,
the end of my urinary catheter has become detached and I am
drenched.[20]

Laura could not hear the high-pitched sound that ricocheted
round the landscape – or void – of his unremitting condition,
and maintained that the passage did not reveal Bauby to be in
actual pain. As far as she was concerned, pain can only be that *rat-
gnawing* sensation; it cannot include 'nerve-wracking', tortuous
'tickling', or indeed the pain of indignity or loss.

The title is our first signpost to the depths of his condition
and how it will be presented; the metaphors represent the weight
and lightness intrinsic to Bauby's perception of the illness: his
body felt as if it was imprisoned in a diving-bell, or a cocoon from
which his 'mind takes flight like a butterfly', enabling him to escape
into imagination and memory.[21] In the Prologue he suggests
that although more people survive strokes due to 'improved
resuscitation techniques', their agony has been 'prolonged and
refined', and despite the paralysis, neuro-transmitters still have
an open pathway to transport messages of pain back and forth
from body to brain. Discomfort – and the title – are emphasised
in the opening lines:

My heels hurt, my head weighs a ton, and something like a giant
invisible diving-bell holds my whole body prisoner.[22]

---

20 Bauby, *The Diving-Bell and the Butterfly*, p.65

21 Bauby, *The Diving-Bell and the Butterfly*, p.13

22 Bauby, *The Diving-Bell and the Butterfly*, p.11

And:

> After their night's respite, my congested bronchial tubes once
> more begin their noisy rattle. My hands lying curled on the
> yellow sheets are hurting although I can't tell if they are burning
> hot or ice cold.[23]

Bauby establishes from the moment he wakes up, he feels
pain; that he is ensconced by an extreme heaviness that is of
both a physical and – with the introduction of his eponymous
metaphor and simile – a psychological nature. He addresses the
wider implications of the pain of his condition in the first chapter;
the moment he realised 'the frightening truth' and accepts his
prognosis of 'official quadriplegic' he remarks that 'the truth was
keener than a guillotine blade'.[24] Bleeding through the subtext is
the unsaid: that the reality is more painful than being beheaded.

Laura's opinion might have been shaped by Bauby's decision
not to list his 'varieties of pain'. It was his intention that *The Diving-
Bell and the Butterfly* should read like 'bedridden travel notes'[25]
from the realms of his locked-in syndrome and, integrated within,
a guide to his assimilation of that region, rather than a book that
chronologically describes every indignity, every discomfort
and every tragedy. Chapter titles and themes – for example
'The Empress' (hospital as museum), '*Cinecittà*' (hospital as
film-set), 'Tourists', 'Paris', 'The Ladies of Hong Kong' – serve
the travelogue form. Bauby is at once guide, touring his new
'kingdom' (the hospital and Berck-sur-Mer), and tourist himself,
sightseeing his past.

---

23 Bauby, *The Diving-Bell and the Butterfly*, p.13

24 Bauby, *The Diving-Bell and the Butterfly*, p.15

25 Bauby, *The Diving-Bell and the Butterfly*, p.13

In 'Tourists' the emphasis is anthropological, focusing on the hospital's population: the 'denizens' include geriatrics, 'a score of comatose patients, poor devils at death's door, plunged into endless night', the morbidly obese and:

> Elsewhere, a battalion of cripples forms the bulk of the inmates. Survivors of sport, of the highway ... these patients remain at Berck for as long as it takes to get their shattered limbs working again. I call them 'tourists'.[26]

It's a pertinent perspective, relatable to any illness, that these survivors – and indeed myself – were mere tourists to the land of extreme condition. There is always someone worse off, in his case the comatose 'poor devils'.

Bauby himself represents the 'broken-winged birds, voiceless parrots, ravens of doom ... Of course we spoil the view.' Resuming his role as guide, as if he had been showing the reader round a zoo, he suggests that the best place to view the 'phenomenon' of these 'broken-winged birds' among the tourists is from the hideout of the rehabilitation room, 'where all patients undergoing physiotherapy are congregated'. They are 'lined up like a row of onions, this human throng waves arms and legs'.[27] Bauby, meanwhile, is 'tethered' amid them for half an hour every morning to an 'inclined board' that is 'slowly raised to a vertical position ... frozen to attention'. Implicit here is his perception of how the patients are viewed, like vegetables, or animals that need to be restrained. His sense of isolation is emphasised, he wants 'to be a part of' the camaraderie below, but when he makes eye contact with his fellow patients they look away; 'feeling the sudden need

---

26 Bauby, *The Diving-Bell and the Butterfly*, p.13

27 Bauby, *The Diving-Bell and the Butterfly*, p.41

to study the ceiling smoke-detector. The tourists must be very worried about fire.' Bauby's irony frequently diffuses pathos.

His imagination roves the world:

Fortunately I have stored away enough pictures, smells and sensations ... to enable me to leave Berck far behind.[28]

He flits from Rangoon to New York to Saint Petersburg: equal to his love of eating was his love of travel, the catalyst in his desire to write 'bedridden travel notes'. His trip to Hong Kong is funded by pure imagination:

This week has been somewhat special. At dawn every day I have flown to Hong Kong ... I have a little trouble finding my way, for unlike many of my other destinations, this city is one I have never actually visited.[29]

Immigrating often requires the learning of language. Not only is the alphabet rearranged for Bauby, but he has speech therapy six days a week:

I am struggling with the letter 'l', a pitiful admission for an editor in chief who cannot even pronounce the name of his own magazine![30]

Progress is made and he celebrates his birthday by pronouncing the alphabet 'more or less intelligibly', even though:

---

28 Bauby, *The Diving-Bell and the Butterfly*, p.111

29 Bauby, *The Diving-Bell and the Butterfly*, pp.111–12

30 Bauby, *The Diving-Bell and the Butterfly*, p.48

It was as if those twenty-six letters had been wrenched from the void; my own hoarse voice seemed to emanate from a far-off country.

He has had to learn the language of his 'far-off country'.

Laura was not convinced by Bauby's portrayal of his condition; she was unable to empathise with the pain of locked-in syndrome. It is true that Bauby does not present himself to be in in constant gnawing, gouging pain, that he tempers his discomfort, sense of loss and loneliness on the shores of his new existence between the tissue layers of metaphor, place and irony. But it is this very layering that succinctly conveys the monstrousness of his condition, showing that pain is a place, and not confined to a blinding sensation.

Hilary Mantel took Virginia Woolf's 'poverty of language' proclamation to task: in her essay 'Meeting the Devil', she asks 'what of the whole vocabulary of singing aches, of spasms and strictures and cramps … the pricking, the pinching? … All good words. All old words.'[31]

Mantel maintains that 'Pain may pass beyond language, but it doesn't start beyond it. The torture chamber is where people "speak",'[32] and Bauby's diving-bell is certainly his 'torture chamber' from which he communicates.

The language we speak is dependent on the place we inhabit. Part of the fun of going on holiday is code-breaking, rolling a new language off your tongue with varying degrees of success; conversely, the trauma experienced by refugees can be exacerbated by being unable to communicate in the language of the country to which they have fled. I didn't talk much in hospital,

---

31   Hilary Mantel, 'Meeting the Devil', in Meeting the Devil, ed. London Review of Books, (London: William Heinemann, 2013), pp.3–17

32   Hilary Mantel, Giving Up the Ghost, p.3

during my tourist's city break to the 'far-off country'; I was busy concentrating on the minute-by-minute effort of being. Yet when I returned home, it was as if I had been speaking another language while away; I was shocked to find giant holes in my vocabulary, and even found myself stuttering. I spent the recuperative period reading: replenishing my stash of words, and constantly checking them in the dictionary. Our language may be interrupted in pain; the words, though, are always there.

Chapter Three

The High Dependency Unit is in whiteness. I'm the only bed left in here.

The walls and floor gleam and glare, so brightly that I squint at the clock as if it's the sun – it's 11 a.m. Fumes of bleach and sprayed disinfectants flay my nostrils. It's a breathtaking concoction. I wonder why the machines around me are bleeping louder, they are more pronounced against this whiteness; alpine acoustics, like the pistol crack of twigs snapping under boot, in snow. And then I realise it's because they're performing solo, and not in chorus with the other patients' monitors.

Find her a bed down on the wards, one where she'll be observed, Mr Palazzo told his entourage that had gathered round my bedside during his early ward round. They had all nodded in agreement, an easy thing to arrange. Shortly afterwards, I watched my fellow patients wheeled off in their beds, vanishing round a corner; even the young woman who had arrived next to me in the middle of the night has gone. My pillows had rucked halfway down my back again, and the nurse who tended her had had such an open face, I willed her to look in my direction. To make eye contact. Perhaps then she might notice that I'm lying askew the buckled pillows. Her stubby ponytail had jiggled as she shook the girl's legs,

'Come on Rachel, wake up … there's a Mars bar waiting for you.' The girl had muttered something, her words sodden with sleep.

'You haven't been taking your insulin. Your brother found you at the bottom of the stairs. Can you remember, Rachel? Rachel?'

Rachel's legs flinched and I saw her crumpled figure at the bottom of a staircase. In grey and blue tones.

'He had to break in, Rachel ... see what happens when you don't take your insulin?' Rachel's body twisted under the white bedcovers. I closed my eyes at that moment. Just to test. A red brick hurtled towards me; then it slowed like a hoverfly as it crumbled mid-air, dissolving into gargoyle, red eyes and curled-back lips. His knobbly fingers clenched another red brick to his chin; he chucked it in my direction, the brick disintegrated, and my eyes shot open for the rest of the night.

'We're sterilising this side of the unit. But we're still trying to find you a bed, so you can stay put for the time being.' A nurse had explained the mass bed exodus to the other side of Critical Care that I had not known existed. 'The good news is that the doctors want to see how you manage without the nasogastric tube.' She placed a large dressing over my chest and proceeded to peel off the tape that had secured the tube to my right nostril.

'Right, just gonna turn off suction, and disconnect ... now take a nice deep breath for me ... one, two, three ...' And the longest udon noodle in all of Japan was pulled out of my nose. Just as she dabbed away the last bit of debris from my face, five figures dressed in white overalls, masks, gloves and blue disposable shoe covers had entered the ward. The cleaners could have passed for a forensics team at a crime scene as they set to work, scrubbing, spraying and polishing every conceivable surface and piece of equipment; wiping away all evidence of life.

'Goodness. What have you got there?' My mother has just arrived – it's 1 p.m. – the unit had alerted her of my move. She's torn between acknowledging the dazzling emptiness of HDU, the lingering aroma of chemicals, and the mug that is in front of me, on a side table pulled over my bed. It's a joke mug; the handle weighs about fifteen kilos.

'Delicious,' I say of the Cup-a-Soup, its saltiness dancing over my tongue. It's the first food I've had, other than ice cubes, and I'm smiling.

'I can't believe these fumes are doing you any good,' she says, nose wrinkling, 'Let me see what's happening, they must've found somewhere for you by now.' My mother heads off in the same direction as the beds this morning.

'I agree; it's probably not the best place for you to be right now. Thing is, there's not enough room for you on the other side,' says the darker haired of the two nurses that have returned with my mum. I don't recognise either of them from the past few days. They disconnect me from the monitors, reconnect my oxygen to a small canister, unplug my bed and then push it – and my two IV stands – through some big swing doors, out of HDU and park me up on the corridor by the lift.

'That's better. No fumes out here,' says the blonder one. It's true; I begin to breathe easier.

'So how long do you think it'll be until Harriet's moved?' I spot acidity lurking under the silky cloak of my mother's patient tone.

'Unfortunately, we've had some difficulty placing Harriet on the ward we wanted, they're full. But 4 South have said they'll take her in the next hour … so one of us will be back to take her down when they're ready, okay?' The darker-haired nurse looks at my mother before they both swipe their security passes through the card reader that opens the doors for them back onto Critical Care.

In the end, discharge from the unit is managed with military precision: checklists completed; sister, nurse and a porter accompany us, and hand me, and a bookish file of notes, over to the nurses' station at 4 South. Staff Nurse Elspeth has a grandmotherly air as she directs the porter into the rectangular, eight-bedded ward, and to the space that has been left for my bed. Shiny high-tech has been replaced with shabby not-so-chic cubicle curtains that she pulls around us; she reconnects my oxygen to the main supply while my mother and I look at one another slightly bewildered by the new environment. I imagine it's like moving from five-star to a tired B&B.

'Well, this is exciting,' says my mother, her cheerfulness seeking to reassure me that I'm on my way to recovery. I am already relieved to be out of Critical Care. To be closer to normality.

Elspeth returns after about an hour, to see how we're getting on. A swarm of ants have gathered in the middle of my back. I can't reach the itch. She leans me forward and discovers that a blister has formed, about three inches long.

'Oh, what's caused that?' my mother asks, all casualness.

'It could be any number of things,' says Elspeth, covering it with a non-stick dressing. The cause is of no concern to me. My brain continues to eliminate questions. Of far more interest is the perfectly domed architecture of a blister. I picture my scalded foot as a child, and I wonder how a blister's tented delicacy accommodates the bulge of fluid. But that's nothing compared to a drop of dew clinging to the pinnacle of a blade of grass, I remind myself.

Lights out at ten. Less incessant bleeping. Opposite is an elderly lady, Doris, her burnt arms and hands swathed in bandages. She sits up, framed by long, wild, grey hair, wailing in confusion. With her round eyes, and mouth contorted in a wide-open oval, I see the swirls of Edvard Munch screaming. I want to comfort her. I can only buzz for a nurse.

An auxiliary nurse sits with Doris for a while, and from time to time is joined by a colleague. It's soothing, listening to their hushed gossipy *Hello*-infused whispers; I catch snippets of Paul and Heather McCartney's divorce proceedings and phone-tapping; of a living room about to be painted lilac. My deluxe HDU 'waterbed' does not feel like the same bed. Every single bone in my body is aching; it feels as if I am lying on a sack of metal rods. I attract their attention but they can't see anything wrong with the bed. When my obs are checked, the nurse cannot find a problem either.

Earlier in the evening, four white-coated doctors pulled the curtains around my bed. For a moment I wondered if they were disguised members of the HDU cleaning gang. 'We're The Pain Team,' their leader announced, flicking her fringe away from her eyes. The gesture had startled me; it was reminiscent of a games mistress who had not been in my mind for years, the one who failed in her mission to acquaint me with a lacrosse stick and the art of cradling – a technique that keeps the ball in the stick's net, away from the opposition's defenders, when the player sprints hell-for-leather up the pitch to have a shot at goal:

I watch the rest of my class practice, the sporty ones run – the wind in their hair – with hush-a-bye babies rocked on high; weaving around the less successful attempts and their squawking infants that roll off into the rhododendron bushes skirting the pitch. My imagination has been so preoccupied with setting the scene to nursery rhyme, that it scuppers my own efforts at maintaining my lacrosse stick lullabied and laden, *And down will fall baby ... Cradle and all.*

'Your grip on the stick needs to be much lighter,' Miss Green advises, her fingertips pushing at her fringe.

'You just need to give the pump a *gentle* squeeze,' the Pain Team captain said, a time-mirrored image of my sports teacher.

They had attached a pump via one of my drips that allowed me to control my pain relief; however, I am on a mission to be rid of the gargoyles, so am not using it. Instead, at 1.30 a.m., I buzz the nurse for paracetamol. At 2.15 a.m. she arrives. She thinks the bed's okay. The gargoyles must be playing tricks.

It's funny how a team has herded up Pain, the thing that slips and slides through the fingers of your mind when you try to pin it down with words. I think of the Brecon mountainside, Pen-y-Fan, mottled with fluffy, flickering will-o'-the-wisp lambs, they don't have faces as such, more a ghostly grimace that expresses their breed characteristic: hhhhhheadache bleats one, bbbbbbbbboneache bleats another, vvvvvvomit bleats a scrawny one. The Pain Team's collies must have keen noses, I decide.

'On a scale of one to ten, where ten is the most painful, how would you rate your pain?' A herding tactic. Right now it could be a seven or perhaps an eight and I'm wide-awake, distracting myself from counting down the hours and minutes before I can have some more paracetamol. I focus on my fellow inmates.

Diagonally opposite me, and nearest the door, is a long-termer, Isla. Moments after The Pain Team had left and my mother had kissed me goodbye, she came over to my bed, half on tiptoe as if the floor was scorching the soles of her feet.

'So what are you in for?' It sounded more of an accusation than a question. I pulled the sheets up to my chin; fortunately, she didn't wait for an answer.

'God, I've been here since before Christmas, coming up fourteen weeks now. Not just on this ward, of course ...'

As she speaks, I fight to place an encroaching sense of trepidation; the feeling you get when starting somewhere new. A purple Mini flashes into mind, an endless drive, a huge Regency-pillared building, smell of polish, that very same rhododendron-laced lacrosse pitch, acoustics that played looking-glass to my voice, an elephant soft toy, loneliness:

My hand skims the mahogany banister that meanders down the stone staircase; Nancy Charter chatters next to me. Her skin is exotically golden; her short white-blond hair is clipped back, and her blue eyes blink like Emily's Tiny Tears doll – the one whose hair I have recently chopped off with nail scissors.

'Mrs Burroughs can get really batey. Mandy S had to sit under The White Table for hours last week, just for talking after lights out.'

I have already decided not to get on the wrong side of the glass-eyed matron. My body is still juddery from the journey in my mother's Mini; home feels a zillion miles away. There's emptiness in my chest, colder than ice cream; I can't remember any of the girls in Enid Blyton having felt like this, except for perhaps that drip Gwendolyn.

'Right, I'll show you the JCR first.' Nancy jumps the last few steps, slap-bang into the path of a towering girl, her arms folded.

'Are you American?' She looks me up and down. 'Nancy only talks to American new girls … Just because she lives in the Bahamaaaaas.'

Nancy walks straight past.

'You're not allowed in the SCR until you're at least ten.' Her hands twist the brass knob of a looming door. The Junior Common Room's olive linoleum is a seething mass of girls, identically dressed in green and white gingham, sitting cross-legged, playing jacks and cards. A girl in front of us jumps up, spooky as a circus clown; faces leap out, some grinning, laughing; others glaring. Thuds of small bouncy balls dart under and over squealing laughter and the slamming of locker doors; I watch Nancy pick her way through the lily pads to a group that noisily welcome her, she squeezes into their circle and immediately shrieks encouragement to the girl tossing the ball and scooping up the star-spiked jacks.

I blink away the scene of my first day at Rookesbury Park School.

'Do you know what I mean?' Isla was still talking. I nod, not knowing at all.

'... Going home in a couple of days. Don't know how I'm going to cope, we're on the seventeenth floor; reckon I'll be a prisoner up there,' she says, gathering her lengthy hair and roping it over her shoulder. 'Got to be careful because they can't do *this* again'. Isla takes a step backwards and pulls her nightdress up to her knickers so I can see the neat, livid red tracks that zip groin to ankle on each spaghetti-stick leg. 'No, Ian – that's my consultant – he's told me that I can't be opened up like this again. Don't know if Alan appreciates that, *you'll be fine Isla* he keeps saying, usually right before he tells me how much he's missed my chicken pies, he's had enough of ready-made meals. The neighbours have given up on him; he's a grumpy sod, barely ever passes the time of day with them. Lizzie's sick of him, decamped to her dad's, which has really given Al the hump. He's peeved enough that Jake spends so much time here. *Sometimes I dunno why you bothered divorcing him, if he's not by your bedside he's texting you.* Sometimes I wonder myself. Jake and I ... we can do each other's Rubik's cubes, do you know what I mean? We can sort each other's colours easily; I can tell him anything, he's my best mate and he's always there for me in spite of what happened. He's a good dad, too. He's told Lizzie that as soon as I get out, she's got to get back home. To be honest, I don't know where I'd be without Jake ... Al's out in his cab all hours, and Lizzie, well, she's a good girl and she cares about me, yes she does, but she's a teenager and she's got her boyfriend and her social calendar. And teens are like toddlers with those hormones chasing round, aren't they? One minute she's like, *Oh Mum, I miss you so* and she's up on the bed for a cuddle, then the next minute she's mouthing off that she has to bring me in clean laundry; *Can't Dad or Al do it? I'm fed up with having to do everything.* "What's *everything*?" I ask, and then that's it, she goes off on one.' Isla's supper arrives at that point; she tiptoes jaggedly back to her chair. I catch my breath.

One of my five pillows falls softly to the floor with the thud of a snowflake. It's directly below me, within arm's reach, a mile away.

A nurse comes in.

'Go on love, geme a nice mugatea.' It's apple-cheeked and bouncy-curled Naomi, next to Isla the only one other than me to still be awake; she checked in earlier this evening.

'Is that why you buzzed?' asks the nurse, irritation lining her face.

'Yes love, I'm fair parched, be an angel.'

'No, I'm afraid I've got far more important things to do,' says the nurse, pouring her out a glass of water. Naomi's a double leg amputee, caused by diabetes, and is rosily relaxed. She doesn't give up, and buzzes again, but her request is met with even shorter shrift. Every couple of hours she swings herself from bed to wheelchair, and waving at me, she spins off to the hospital entrance for a fag break, in nothing but a thin nightdress. Apparently her kidneys are giving her problems.

And then there is Faith, awaiting vascular surgery. When I first noticed her, she was leaning on crutches, talking to Isla in cut-glass English tones. She had her back to me and seemed petite and elegant, dressed head-to-toe in black with her hair cut in a glossy hennaed, geometric bob. When she turned round, her red-rimmed eyes – sunken within an Elizabethan pallor – were as dark as a starless sky, it seemed they were without irises, and her lids were blackened with kohl. Her eyes bored into mine, and then she had very nimbly turned on her crutches and clunked back to bed, continuing her conversation with Isla, but in a bloodlessly lipped, broad Belfast accent.

She's living at a drugs rehabilitation hostel in Shepherd's Bush. 'It's right near the market, so it is. Got a tidy room, all brand new with doors onto the garden.'

'See the birds from your bed, do you?' says Naomi, from the end of her bed.

'Aye. Pigeons on the scrounge.' Faith's mobile rings.

She rams it into her cheek; wodges of skin pouch angrily either side.

'Right, I already told yer, Dahlin'. Jimmy's got the gear ... C'mon, yer know Jimmy, Charlie's mate ... Yep. By the taxi stand. Three o'clock. He'll find yer ... Yep at the station ... No! Donchya ever listen? Hammersmith ... It's only a bit. Ah'm goin outta my head. But it'll keep me goin. They're a right crowd of stooges in here ... Docs? Oh c'mon, gimme a break, they couldn't give a feckin shit ... Of course yer'll have to pay him ... A ton. Ah'll give it you back ... Aye, when youse get here, Dahlin' ...Yeah, yeah, ah got it.'

The pillows have gone AWOL again and I'm desperate to be lying flat; according to the nurses I need to remain sitting upright. This once rippling bed is not helping – it feels like its own skeleton has embedded itself into my skin. It's 6.15 a.m. at last, and I buzz for more para.

A charge nurse answers my call from a different section of 4 South. At first he's abrupt, but when he returns with paracetamol, he brings a clean pillowcase and rearranges the jigsaw behind my back.

'My bed ... feels different, I'm aching,' I say, warmed by his kindness. He prods the mattress from different angles and shakes his head when he discovers that my bed hadn't been plugged in to the mains, and that in its deflated state I have, since my arrival on this ward fourteen hours ago, been languishing on the bed's metal framework.

There's no Mr Palazzo to regiment ward rounds; we're all unkempt when the various consultants and their entourages appear for ward rounds during breakfast. Isla hails hers as if they are friends. I have no idea who mine are … they are a different lot to those I saw on HDU. About six of them. *Hello* they say, before gathering round the end of my bed and poring over my clipboarded notes in discussion; they do not introduce themselves and they don't ask me any questions.

'When can I go home?' I interrupt their nods and half-smiles of goodbye. The ruddy-cheeked man who has led the huddled discussion steps forward.

'We have to monitor your Angiomyolipoma and the haematoma for a while longer, make sure there's no further bleeding or infection, but in any event we can't send you home before you're a little more mobile. So, we'll organise some physio. Okay?' He nods goodbye, there's no pause for a response, and they leave.

A washing-up bowl of warm water is wordlessly put down on the table by my bed; water slaps over the sides onto a clean gown. Joy that I have the independence now to wash myself is momentary, and gives way to awareness that the table is just out of reach. *Come on Harriet, don't be pathetic!* As I attempt to sit up and stretch over, there's a stunning pain that zigzags up and down my body, and a simultaneous zinc-white flash in front of my eyes. I try again, and the pain is spiked with barbed wire. I worry about using the buzzer, not wanting to bother the nurses with anything trivial. So I wait until an orderly comes by and ask him to move my table nearer, and for the back of my gown to be undone. He's built like a heavyweight boxer, yet his movements and manner are gossamer-gentle. *Would you like me to give you a hand with washing?* he asks before he goes. *I'll be fine, thank you for your help,* I smile. And it is so liberating to be able to wash myself. It had been unnerving in HDU, having the male nurse chat about his attractive wife – *she really takes care of herself; she's immaculate ... oh look, you're dirty down there, you're bleeding, your period started? ... No, no need to apologise; I'm a hands-on dad and do my fair share of changing nappies. Nothing makes me squeamish,* he'd chuckled.

I dip my toothbrush into the glass of water and load it with the fennel toothpaste my mother brought yesterday – an alternative to mint, from which my palate suddenly recoiled, as if it were neat horseradish. The fennel is gentle and refreshing, and my mouth feels nice. As I brush, I think how lucky I am, *she anticipates my every need.*

Now to change the gown. Reaching under it, loosened, to wash was fine; the problem remains of how to take it off *unseen*:

The sea is roaring, and I'm at Polzeath and the beach where my father, Emily and I spent several childhood summers with our cousins. I hide between rocks, and wrap a towel around me, one arm on guard for any sneaking gust of wind that may ambush my quest for modesty while I perform a hunched-up, hopping dance during which I exchange my swimming costume, drenched from charging waves, with clothes that have somehow become damp and sandy themselves.

It was a process I undoubtedly made more complicated than it needed to be. Here my progress is impeded by the tubing that sprouts from each hand, and the IV stands. I have no choice now but to buzz for assistance. A nurse arrives, and pulls the curtains around the bed; I relax at once, snug in the privacy of my cubicle, as she disconnects the lines and stoppers the cannula before replacing my gown. After, when she swishes the curtains open, the ward is blinding.

*

'Good, that's great Harriet.'

I am standing, gripping onto a walking frame.

'Okay, I've got control of your IV stands and catheter bag. Yes, and the back of your gown … So, just lift the frame … that's right … yup about 15cm in front of you, now step into it with your right foot … and follow with your left … Well done, that's excellent!'

'My legs, they're heavy,' I say to Alison, the physio, 'my stomach too.' When I look down, I'm struck again by how I could be mistaken for reaching the end of a twin pregnancy; my tummy is still obese with haematoma.

'Yeah, I think you've got a lot of nerve disruption going on, but you're doing fine.'

I almost get as far as Isla's bed, and although it's rather a shuffle, my journey back is much more confident.

'Okay Harriet, that's a great effort, tomorrow we'll venture out of the ward,' Alison says, adjusting the pillows behind my back. I feel bubbles of euphoria tingling as I wave goodbye. Escape is nigh.

It's a pale young woman that turns up to see Faith. The bottle of wine she pulls from her rucksack is snatched from her hands and expertly decanted into a Ribena bottle, and then Faith stuffs a package down the front of her top before taking off to the bathroom, clunk, clunk, clunk, clunk. The girl waits, twiddling her nose stud round and round. My mother, on her afternoon visit, peers at me from round the side of her newspaper and raises her eyebrows theatrically to make sure I've seen what she's seen.

'This is my daughter,' announces Faith to the ward, returning both to bed and to Received Pronunciation. Daughter squirms in her chair, head bent.

'Never mind that … you promised, Mum.' Her words are barely audible from behind a lank blond curtain.

'And you'll get it, just as soon as I find my purse, darling,' purrs her mother as she pours herself a glass of Ribena.

A familiar figure stands in the ward doorway. Anders, my brother-in-law, scans the beds as he walks through. His smile settles on me like a sudden shaft of sunlight.

'You don't look half as bad as I thought you'd look,' he says, sitting on the end of my bed. I have no idea how I look. Emily brushes my hair every day, *I've got a mirror in my handbag* she's offered, but on each occasion I shake my head. I don't want to look at myself. Anders chats on about the latest shenanigans of Alice and Maddy, my nieces, and I move on into their world, buoyed by his presence. He doesn't seem to mind that I don't say much. After he goes, I remember being struck by his warmth and easy manner all those years ago, when he and Emily were at school together.

A nurse and a porter arrive at my bedside. I'm off for a scan.

Outside the confines of the ward, life shudders past as if I'm standing in the central reservation of the M25, buffeted by juggernaut after juggernaut; the blur of normality makes me giddy. My bed is pushed through Imaging, past reception and the waiting outpatients who sit reading, chatting, studying their phones, to a space allocated for beds like mine. The nurse stands on sentry duty. As people pass I notice their eyes tracing the snaking tubes. We are there for an age. I gorge on the verdancy in the pastoral murals ahead, losing myself in the lush shades, until all the greens merge.

Pale sage green walls … it is my first day at Lampeter, and I sit on the bed contemplating my cell. Lloyd Thomas Hall of Residence – or Lloyd Tom, as it is affectionately known – had been renovated some thirty years previously in the '60s, by a Swedish architect who designed prisons. He was an interesting choice considering the imposing 1820s heart of the college, and the spectacular Teifi Valley framework. *What on earth possessed you to choose this university, literally in the middle of nowhere, and one that no one's ever heard of??* I shrink in front of smirking Incredulity, and desperately root around the pockets of my mind. I fish out the decision-making, scrunched-up balls of reason, and smooth them flat like the foil of Kit-Kats. Five wrappers:

One: The fervour of an alumnus, my A-level history teacher, 'nowhere else like it … it was far out, man,' he'd said hypnotically – in one of our extracurricular discussions – with Crosby, Stills and Nash's 'Southern Cross' playing in the background.

Two: My perverseness, when fifth choice Lampeter had been rubbed out by The Powers That Be from my pencil-drafted UCAS form.

Three: The soulful journey from Swansea to Carmarthen, where the train had dipped in and out of the Celtic Sea on my way to interview.

Four: That Lampeter most certainly was in the middle of green nowhere.

Five: The interview itself.

The stern-faced Head of English had greeted me in the department corridor with a Thomas Hardy poem.

'Take a few minutes to look at this, will you.' She disappeared behind a door before reappearing what seemed like only seconds later.

'Come in, come in!' she said as if I was very, very late, ushering me in to a solemn, book-lined room.

'Read the poem aloud. Afterwards I'd like you to talk about it until I tell you to stop.'

I was in love with Hardy the novelist, obsessed with *Tess*, but woefully ignorant of his poetry; there was definitely enough rope to hang myself several times over. And my brain was not feeling at its sharpest. I had got off the Carmarthen bus in Lampeter High Street an hour and a half early for the interview; instead of touring the campus and library, I had found myself – at 11.45 a.m. – walking through the doors of the net-curtained Ivy Bush Inn. The pub hum had stalled to a staccato stop, as I made my way to the bar.

'Half a pint of dry cider, please,' I asked at the bar, acutely aware of my prim English accent, of being the only female in the vicinity of about thirty wellington-booted Welsh-speaking farmers, and of my reddening cheeks. There was a chorus of *Duw duw duw* and then the lilting Welsh hum took up again.

After an hour or so, the Head's face had softened. She gave me an unconditional offer, there on the spot. At its crudest level, I was in no position to turn it down, being such a successfully useless examinee.

Back in my Lloyd Thom room. *Yeah, isn't that reason enough?* Incredulity crumbles, my turn to snigger. *But did not Fate play his hand?* Thomas Hardy pushes open the door and pulls up the chair that had been tucked under the desk. *What about your father?* he continues, leaning back and twisting the end of his moustache. *Oh, Mr Hardy!* I blush at his presence. He's just as I had imagined, with his domed forehead and tweed suit. *How kind of you to join. Yes, you have a point, sir.* And he did, it was only after I accepted my place at the university that my father told me he'd spent three years in Lampeter when his school had been evacuated to the college itself during the war. Lampeter. Of all places.

As I sit deciphering the Morse-coded drawing-pin holes, woodwormed into the wall over the desk by previous students, I hear my grandmother's voice.

'I do wish you'd be more gregarious,' she said. Nom, my father's mother (Nonna to the other grandchildren; I'd mispronounced it as a young child) often wished this, and it was always said in the same tone that she said, 'Why do you have to have all that hair flopping over your face?' and, 'Oh! It'd be so nice to see you wear bright colours one day.' Her words tolled with martyred disappointment … but it was always the greg*a*rious that pinched; mostly because of the way she stressed the second syllable, it seemed that I would never be such a glamorous-sounding word. Nom certainly would not approve of me sitting there, decoding drawing-pin hole patterns.

After some cajoling, the hermit emerges, blinking in the light; I leave my room and knock on the door opposite. There is the scrape of a chair, but no answer. I knock again. A few long seconds tick by before the door is flung open, and a pair of lips confronts me. They are gigantically rouge in every dimension, the bounciest of mattresses; they ridicule the bully who had taunted me with *Jagger lips!* and a racist alternative jibe.

'Yesssss?????' they hiss, barely parting.

'Ummmmmm … Er … Hi. I'm Harriet,' I say, relieved to have found her eyes. 'Ummm I'm opposite you … just wondered if you're settling in okay and …' and my words trail off into the desert-distance between us. Her amber stare drills into me for a few more long seconds.

'Right. Well, if that's it …' And the door closes in my face.

That's how I meet Tania, my best friend.

Greens have been replaced by hues of white and grey. It takes six of them to transfer me across to the scanning bed. It's the first time I've lain flat, it's excruciating, a mediaeval rack. And freezing. A button is pushed and the CT scanner groans over me; the radiographers disappear – not before attaching one of my cannulas to another tube.

'Right Harriet, just follow the breathing instructions. Don't be alarmed if you feel a warm rush, it's contrast dye.'

I visualise my face purpling with the effort of holding my breath, and now, when I can't hold it any longer, it escapes like a deflating balloon. Syrupy warmth seeps into my bladder, infrared; it is the contrast dye.

Back to the ward and to one of Faith's rants. The wall behind her bed is a screen and she's a livid projection, I watch her fitful movements silhouetted like shadow puppetry.

'If it's not the skebs, it's the skitters,' she says to no one in particular, 'it's flowin outta me hoop quicker than the Blackwater, so it is.'

'Oh, have you got diarrhoea?' Naomi's all smiles.

'You wah?'

'Got the squits?'

'Aye … the skitters, cramping up me belly. Feckin docs are next to useless, so they are.'

'You need to get a load of water down you, girl!'

'Nah, this is the best medicine,' scowls Faith, swigging from her bottle of Ribena. Naomi's still smiling; if she has registered Faith's switch in accent, she doesn't show it.

Saturday morning and we're home alone, so scant is the nursing presence.

Yesterday my mother brought me an orchid. 'A Phalaenopsis,' she said, knowing that this botanical titbit would amuse me. As talented as my mother is, she is not known for her green fingers. It sits in a glazed ceramic pot on my table. Six lemon leopard faces peek out from blossoms teetering on the skyscraper double stem; their eyes, ears, mouths and whiskers are dotted out in crimson; and each leopard is suspended by a pair of magnificent angel wings, arctic white petals. Leaves fan out over the pot casting shadows over *The Guardian*; the newspaper lies there weightily idle. Its creases and folds beckon; I have no desire to pick up and read this symbol of a Saturday morning habit. A habit that began at The New Bridge Caff, over their infamous all-day brekkie, half people-watching, half catching up with the world at large. This greasy spoon was frequented by Lampeter locals and several student regulars: James, the Philosopher, would always be sitting at the window table, in the same elbow-patched chunky-knit khaki jumper, with tomes of Schopenhauer and Nietzsche piled ostentatiously high while he held court with various female mature students, rarely studying at all. On another table would be Hirut, Ethiopian princess – *so she said*. When she'd finished painting her wildcat nails blood red, she would splay out her fingers to dry, blowing on them from time to time. She'd flash a blinding smile at Megan and order a coffee. Once they were dry, Hirut produced her pouch of goodies, shrugged her shoulders free from her leopard-skin coat, and started to roll immaculately taloned joints.

I doubt The New Bridge existed in my father's time.

Dear All, Lampeter a quiet old Welsh town has been invaded by Yanks, he wrote home on 31 October 1943, aged twelve. *They are all over the place. Not that it is a bad thing mind you but they are a bit noisy. They brighten the old place up you know. I asked one of their number, 'Got any gum, chum?' and guess what, he gave me a piece!*

How could I have not wanted to listen to his Lampeter tales when he visited me at Dolau Gwyrdion Uchaf, the cottage I rented in my second year? I was too incensed by his insistence on renaming Piers, my boyfriend, 'Horatio Goodfellow' to want to listen to anything he had to say. And by his drinking, of course.

My gaze falls on the newspaper again. Picking it up is as likely as lacing up a pair of hiking boots right now. All the pages and text are as overwhelming as Himalayan terrain, and as befuddling as the first occasion I read a newspaper:

'Yes, of course you can watch *Sesame Street*, thing is I'm not sure what time it's on.' I follow Daddy, newspaper under his arm, into the living room.

'But I've got a new game for you, a kind of treasure hunt,' he says smiling, and placing *The Observer*, and all its supplements, down on the carpet in front of me with a tah-dah flourish.

'Why don't you read through the newspaper until you find the television pages, let me know what time *Sesame Street* starts ... I'll watch it with you.'

'But Daddy, I thought you could tell me,' says four-year-old me.

'Don't you remember what I told you about Thought, Sweetheart?'

'No,' I say.

'Well, he planted a feather and thought a chicken would grow
… now crack on, or we'll miss Ernie and Bert.' And my father leaves
me to it.

I unfold the paper. The pages are huge – big enough to make
myself an outfit – and they crackle as I turn them over, one by one. I
have just started to read, but the words are a lot bigger in the picture
books at Miss Freeman's school. I squint at the tiny print, seeking all
the S-words. It takes forever, and the words rub off onto my fingers,
but at long last I find a page which looks different to the rest. Days
of the week and numbers. S-u-n-d-a-y, goody, that's today, and my
forefinger traces down the column looking for more S's. The words
are even tinier here, but it doesn't have far to travel now, to find
S-e-s-a-m-e S-t-r-e-e-t.

I shift against my pillows, and revisit that same bay-windowed
living room, and see myself sitting on the floor, leaning against the
mile-long, bottle-green velvet sofa, and watch my forty-one-year-
old father placing the newspaper in front of me, he's wearing black
trousers, a black polo neck – he always wore polo necks – and he's
still wearing his sheepskin jacket as we'd just come in from walking
our dogs, to the Burton Pynsent monument. That jacket lasted for
years, he was wearing it the day he returned Emily and me back to
Rookesbury Park after an exeat when Miss Epps, a younger matron,
had been particularly giggly and pink-faced in his presence.

'Has your Daddy remarried, Harriet?' she asked afterwards.

'No.'

'Well, has he got a girlfriend then?' More giggling as she stroked
the frame of his photograph on my bedside cabinet.

Back then he had the face of Cary Grant, with a hint of Robbie Williams around the eyes and his nose-to-mouth laughter lines – which I inherited right from childhood. Later, his face got all puffed out.

I imagine him coming to visit me here.

'Oh! You poor little dab!' he would have said.

*

'Here you go, Sissy.' Emily puts the new dressing gown she's bought me round my shoulders. I run the fabric between my thumb and forefinger, it's as if I'm experiencing softness for the first time, and I sink deep into this enveloping luxuriousness. I had been feeling chilly; my heart twists at her thoughtfulness and generosity.

In the last few days a couple of patients have gone home, including poor Doris. A headmistressish sort has taken her bed; I wonder what she makes of Faith, who is busy directing her venom at the nurses.

'C'mere, you,' she says to one. 'Gis a hand with getting this frickin thing off.' She has started unravelling the bandage that's wound round her right leg.

'Faith. You know the doctors have said this needs to stay on.' The nurse firmly rebinds her leg.

'Ow! Careful will ya? Got any idea how sore it is?' Faith snatches the bandage out of the nurse's hand.

'That's why the doctors say ...'

'Listen, Blondie, give ma head some peace, why not. Ah'm sick of them and their faffin about. Eejits the lot of youse.' Faith swings the metre or so of crepe bandage above her head as if it were a lasso.

Blondie has to call for backup to get Faith's leg rebandaged. The same scenario is played out four or five times. Interspersed with this are her inordinate periods spent in the bathroom, followed by louder and increasingly graphic complaints of uncontrollable diarrhoea. The Ribena, however, continues to be going down a treat. At the other end of the ward, Naomi's posse of visitors is staying late and they have brought in fish and chips, which stink out the ward.

Lights off. Try to sleep on happily inflated bed. Upright. Can't turn. Pillows slip. Gargoyles grimace. Sheets heavy. Still aching all over. Quit moaning. Try thinking nice thoughts, this New Year in Ferryside, but brain not cooperating. Back to clock-watching for paracetamol. Naomi wheels off down the ward for her fag breaks; she has more success with her tea requests tonight.

Out of nowhere I'm heaving with nausea. I buzz for a nurse and she brings me a grey cardboard receptacle that looks very much like half an egg box without the divisions – just in time. By daybreak, I am throwing up every ten minutes. There's nothing really to throw up, as I have only been sipping soup here and there. The alarms on my IVs keep going off: bending my elbows to bring the bowl closer to my face seems to kink the cannulas or tubes, and the nurses look irritated when they have to repeatedly investigate the alarm, straighten the lines, and replace the bowl. I hear tutting too, from Faith.

Miserable day. Too sick for my ablutions, or to sit in the chair. I am aware of the retinue that arrives to take Isla home, of her daughter in a huff and of the angry kerfuffle that arises from Faith for ignoring the nil-by-mouth sign above her bed, but everything is making me vomit: the kitchen smells that infect the ward an hour before mealtimes; the seemingly constant stream of takeaways; Faith's diarrhoea rants; but probably the worst of all is the sickly smell of the oxygen cannula clawing my nose.

Emily and my mother have arrived. They sit with me and don't talk much; they take it in turns to empty the bowl and to wipe my face. I hate making them worried.

'What on earth do you think's causing this vomiting?' my mother asks the nurse who's arrived at my bedside with a small trolley.

'We're not really sure,' she says, snapping on surgical gloves. 'But we're taking her off the antibiotics in case she's having a reaction.' She removes the tape that's securing the tubing on my left arm and gently pulls out the line that goes into the top of my hand, then tapes a cotton wool dressing to the site. 'There, that'll be easier for you to manage just the one IV now,' she says, patting my arm.

Alison the physio comes, but goes. I'd wanted to show off my progress. The Pain Team returns.

'Harriet, you don't seem to have been using your painkilling pump, aren't you in any pain?' asks the Miss Green lookalike.

'No. Yes ... don't want to hallucinate,' I manage before violently retching again.

'Well, if you don't use it, we'll need to remove it.' More retching.

'Can't you give her something for the nausea?' I hear impatience collide with concern in my mother's voice.

'Yup, we'll write her up for an antiemetic, but Harriet, do try and use the pump too.'

The tiny anti-sickness pill does nothing. If anything the nausea gets worse.

Naomi and Faith are discussing, from opposite ends of the ward, all the Mexican meals they've enjoyed.

'Ooh you know when the melted cheese drips through them tacos? Oh I love that.'

'Too right. And washed down with a nice wormy tequila.'

'Please,' I say, 'could you talk more quietly. Feel so sick.'

Faith is off her bed and on her crutches. She's at my bedside. The sick bowl falls to the floor.

'Whoops-a-daisy,' she says, staring down at me.

She leans in even closer. So her nose is almost touching mine. The alcohol on her breath triggers another rush of nausea.

'What is it, lovey? Cat got your tongue? Again.'

Her eyes are blacker than ever. She flicks the bowl out to the middle of the floor with a crutch. 'See. I can play jolly hockey sticks too.' She enunciates each word deliberately with sneering, red-wine-stained lips, in Received Pronunciation.

I look away.

'Oh, she doesn't want to play, Naomi.' Faith pouts. 'Well then. Here's the deal. You want us to talk quieter? I'll frickin' whisper … if you frickin' shut up. Whaddya say?' Back to broad Belfast.

I open my mouth to speak; bile jets out, down my gown and bedclothes. Faith rolls her eyes at me, and clunks off to the bathroom, cursing loudly.

My cubicle curtains are now perpetually closed. I don't want an audience. Day merges into night. Every sip of water rushes up with volcanic force, erupting through my nose as well as my mouth, eyes streaming. I try and lie as still as I can in the sticky aftermath of each bout. Two members of The Pain Team are back, armed with needles that are pushed into my face, wrists, knees and feet.

'We've had great results with acupuncture for nausea,' says one of them. Each time I vomit a couple of needles pop out, no sooner than they've replaced them, a couple more fall to the floor; they have plenty to spare and I'm jabbed again and again.

The doctors on their ward round are noncommittal and I can find no words to question them.

Emily points out my catheter bag. Evidently it is full to the brim, and bloodied.

'Right,' says my mother, eyes glinting, and without another word disappears off the ward. Emily and I exchange looks.

'I know, sweet pea,' she says, stroking my hair. 'But something needs to be done.'

Whatever my mother says results in the catheter bag being hurriedly emptied, and there's a visit from the Critical Care Matron.

'Okay Harriet, let's see what's been going on,' she says kindly, looking over her glasses at me with a smile. 'I'd like Harriet's obs done now, yes I mean now, in front of me … and perhaps you would find out why she's not wearing compression boots,' she says in a more clipped tone to the nurse that showed her to my bed. Within minutes my oxygen has been increased and my feet are once again encased in the inflatable boots that I wore on HDU. Numerous attempts are made to force down the vile nasogastric tubing.

'It's probably sensible if we move you back up to HDU,' she says.

'No … please not.' Nausea powers up my throat.

'Well, I think it's important to get Harriet stabilised again,' she says to my mother and Emily.

I shake my head. I don't want to be here but returning to HDU will be too many backward steps, miles away from home.

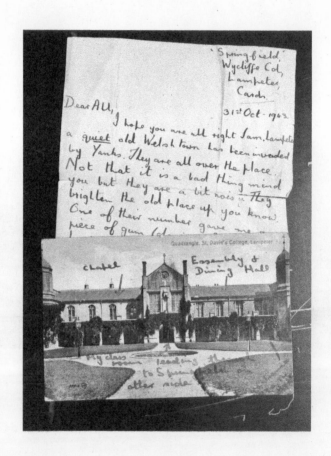

'Springfield'
Wycliffe Col,
Lampeter,
Cards.

31st Oct. 1943.

Dear All,

I hope you are all right I am. Lampeter a quiet old Welsh town has been invaded by Yanks. They are all over the place. Not that it is a bad thing mind you but they are a bit noisy. They brighten the old place up you know. One of their number gave me a piece of gum (at

Quadrangle, St. David's College, Lampeter

Chapel   Assembly &
              Dining Hall

My class room leading to Spring—— the other side

54

Chapter Four

Home (sickness)

Show me the way to go to home (sic)

My first post as a newly qualified English Language teacher was at a language school in Wimbledon and the majority of my students were South Korean, given their 50,000-strong community a couple of miles up the road in New Malden. As I went round the class reciting their names, *Yeong Hye, Gi Jun, Jeong, Sook Hee* ... the look of sweet anticipation on their faces filled me with doubt. Could I/would I fulfil their expectations? It was their first time away from home and my heart pumped with admiration: they had studied English throughout childhood and mastered our entirely different alphabet, but developing their language skills over 5,000 miles away and grappling with a new culture required courage. Without exception they were fiercely proud of South Korea and wanted the language to describe what their culture and *my hometown* meant to them. I themed a week's lessons on Home, and during our learning it occurred to me how the confusing grammar of *home* – noun, adverb and adjective – demonstrated perfectly the chasm spanning its corresponding semantics of place and concept, and its inherent partition of presence and absence. It was fascinating to see how at times home slid beyond translation in both oral and written work, when it came to distinguishing between the physical description of, say, the apartment/neighbourhood they had grown up in, and pinpointing how/why it was home.

The glut of home-centred idioms caused a stir; class favourites included the tapestried *home is where the heart is* and *home sweet home*. Conversation turned to kimchi. Kimchi is the side dish of fermented napa cabbage, radish, garlic, ginger and chilli that's been the staple food of Korea for centuries, a fixture of every mealtime. Nowadays it's a popular superfood, but back then, in 2002, it was largely unknown in the UK. I learned it was synonymous with Korean culture, many families having their own special recipe passed down through the ages. Soon my fridge contained several Tupperware containers of *the best* kimchi. Its scent was even tantalising to my dog, who managed to heist the fridge and retrieve a tub. The class explained that the rituals of making and eating it here in London helped them feel *at home,* and was of comfort in their *homesickness.* They were here to study English in order to improve their job prospects, but for some it also seemed to be a rite of passage that they were expected to complete. *We must endure. Koreans endure. But it really hurts. Worse than military service,* said Tae Su, touching his chest. I was moved by their homesickness, and recognised the physicality of its raw soul-ache,[33] both from boarding school and from the fallout of my parents' divorce. As a small child, home had meant the life I had thus far shared with my parents, and from the age of five, when they split, I felt the stretch; one foot was clamped in London with our mother while the other was wading the Somerset Levels with our father. When with one parent I'd miss the other, and

---

33   Johannes Hofner, a Swiss doctor in the eighteenth century, diagnosed Swiss mercenary soldiers to be suffering from nostalgia: the etymology derives from the Greek *nostos* (return home) and *algos* (pain), combined with eighteenth-century German *heimweh* (homesickness), and gives us *nostalgia*, meaning acute homesickness.

their way of being, and feel an odd sense of incompleteness, that I ought to be somewhere else. Over the years I frequently told school friends that my parents were planning on getting back together. This was not because I was ashamed of the divorce; it was the fantasy idyll of us to be living all together at home again, under one roof, which I definitely knew to be an impossibility.

A vicar inspired the method I chose to elicit the idiom *broken home*. I built a rudimentary house from Lego, with four rooms. In class I drew, on separate scraps of paper, stick figures of woman, man, girl and boy. And into each room I popped a figure. Then, to gratifying gasps, I dropped the house on the floor, Lego and figures went scattering, a fully deconstructed home. For it had been during the summer holidays that, while staying with my father, my sister Emily (6) and I (9) spent one afternoon as merhorses in the Huish Episcopi village swimming pool, with a girl about my age called Lizzie. We had few friends of our own age in Somerset, so when we met her on that blazing August day, Lizzie's invitation to tea dazzled with its sparkle of burgeoning friendship. On the short walk from the pool to her home – the rectory, as it turned out – my imagination had galloped ahead of our chat as I pictured how, when the holiday came to an end, we would write lengthy letters to one another, and plan adventures for our next visit. The vicar held open the rectory's front door and ushered his daughter inside. I remember how her wet plaits smacked his cassock as she turned back to us, cheeks aflame, and in that stolen glance I saw our leaping, neighing creatures splash right out of her eyes. He pulled the door to, until there was only the crack of our new friend visible. A stray, golden strand of hair illuminated the curve of the vicar's stomach. *I'm afraid Lisbeth was mistaken, I cannot allow her to play with children from a broken home,* Lizzie's father repeated, and I could barely spot his lips in the depths of his grey beard, just the dark hole of his mouth. He pointed down the path to the garden gate and we skedaddled. *I thought he was her grandpa*, my sister said to our father when we recounted what had happened. *He was afraid, was he? Well, he'll be more than afraid when he's heard what I have to say*, said Daddy already halfway out the door. And I pictured the dark hole of the vicar's mouth as he'd uttered *broken home*, and from it spewed the rooms of our homes shared with each of our parents, jumbled and as if they'd been broken apart like Lego.

Although the vicar's behaviour had been wholly inappropriate, pun intended, he clearly hit a nerve. I told myself that I had the best of both worlds, living in the city and countryside, having two loving parents. My grandmother sponsored children from famine stricken countries, I had seen their photographs and read their letters and appreciated I was extremely fortunate. I had all this, and yet I knew something to be quietly broken within me, and I couldn't understand why.

The class got *broken home*, and it provoked lively discussion on the stigma of divorce in South Korea, and the idiom's wider implications concerning home and identity. *If someone doesn't feel in their skin, it means their ... home ... no, world broken also*, said Yoon. James Baldwin addressed this sentiment in his 1957 novel *Giovanni's Room*.[34] The narrator is David, a young, white American living in Paris. His girlfriend, Hella, has gone travelling in Spain to decide whether or not she wants to marry him, and in her absence, he falls in love with an Italian barman, Giovanni, with whom he moves in. 'He made me think of home – perhaps home is not a place but simply an irrevocable condition.'[35] Essentially, the Italian makes David feel at home with himself. He says he left America 'in order to find myself ... an interesting

---

34 James Baldwin, *Giovanni's Room*, (London: Penguin Books, 2007)

35 Baldwin, *Giovanni's Room*, p.82

phrase, not current as far as I know in the language of any other people ...' and concludes that if he had known the self he found would be the same one from which he had spent 'so much in flight' he would have 'stayed home'.[36] Giovanni's small room becomes increasingly cell-like and chaotic as their relationship develops and then disintegrates, and Baldwin clearly uses it as a metaphor for all the dimensions of home that he invokes:[37] not feeling at home in one's self, or in the world; and homesickness. On Hella's eventual return, David cannot find the strength to be honest about his sexuality. She departs for the States, which he is unable to do; he cannot imagine himself fitting in at home, his experiences will have made him unrecognisable to those he loves. Baldwin raises the quandary of returning home after an Odyssean absence; will it ever replicate the home *deep imag'd*[38] in one's soul? The address remains on the map, its grid coordinates the same, but to all intents and purposes the building itself may as well have been demolished by a wrecking ball, so unrecognisable has all that it once represented become.

Becoming homeless involves disaster, whether man-made, natural or personal, and world over, is a catastrophic thing; as John Berger wrote, without a home 'everything is fragmentation'.[39] Early in 2001, the documentary filmmaker Linda Hattendorf discovered eighty-year-old Jimmy Mirikitani living on the streets of New York, sheltered by the awning of a Korean store. Mirikitani was a prolific artist, and survived on the streets by selling his work. Hattendorf began filming his life, she was intrigued by

---

36 Baldwin, *Giovanni's Room*, p.18–19

37 When thinking about *Giovanni's Room*, it's hard to ignore the biographical facts that Baldwin moved to Paris in his twenties, exhausted by the obstacles of racial and sexual discrimination in the States, and fell in love with a young Swiss man.

38 'His native home deep imag'd in his soul.' Homer, *The Odyssey*, Book XIII

39 John Berger, *My Heart, Brief as Photos*, (London: Bloomsbury, 2005), p.56

the subject matter of his art: contented Japanese cats; vibrant persimmon fruit (native to Hiroshima); Californian internment camps – stick figure people working alongside more detailed jackrabbits – in the foreground of Hokusaiesque mountains; and red atomic bombs. Jimmy drew these pictures, particularly the internment camp scenes, everyday – sometimes several times a day. The film[40] documents Jimmy at work, in all weathers and temperatures, while Linda questions him about his pictures. His answers tell the story of how he came to be homeless. Although born in Sacramento, Jimmy grew up in Hiroshima, returning to the US at eighteen to avoid military service in Japan and pursue his artistic aspirations in a freer country. He was living with his sister in Seattle when Japan bombed Pearl Harbor. The siblings were separated and sent to internment camps. When Linda meets Jimmy over fifty years later, he is still without his US citizenship and has never found his sister.

In the devastation of the immediate aftermath of 9/11, the New York air is toxic and a coughing Jimmy is a solitary figure on the deserted streets of Soho. Linda invites him to stay with her. The camera tracks the pair's day-to-day living in her one-bedroom apartment. She films as she cooks for them, the camera propped on the kitchen work surface. He sleeps on the floor but his balletic stretches on waking suggest that he has passed the night on the most luxurious of mattresses. While Jimmy completes ever-bigger pictures, Linda begins the process of making friends with the neighbourhood's social services, getting him a social security number and retrieving his passport. Her cat follows them around, yowling bemusement at the new houseguest's presence; as the days pass her wails become less. Space may be tight, but the apartment's homeliness intensifies

---

40 *The Cats of Mirikitani*, by Linda Hattendorf. (USA: Lucid Dreaming Inc, 2006)

their burgeoning grandfather–granddaughter relationship: they watch Samurai movies together; both are anxious when the other returns home later than expected; and it's delightful to watch them bicker, the way families do. When we hear Jimmy laugh as he potters round the apartment playing with the cat, watering and nurturing plants, as he cooks and washes dishes, the sound is exotic. It's as if he has finally relaxed, enough at least to take breaks from his obsessive picture making, and just to be.

Linda facilitates Jimmy's reunion with his sister, and other Mirikitanis living in the US. And in June 2002, we see Jimmy hosting his eighty-second birthday party in his own apartment, found for him by social services. When he moved in, it was brand new and sparkling white. At his party, we see the transformation: his pictures – *my life's work* – adorn the walls; plants inhabit every corner; the cat that he rescued from the street – and which he tellingly introduces as *the castaway cat I bring home* – sits contentedly on the sofa; the table is laid and Jimmy is mingling with new friends. Poignantly, as the film closes, we move from Jimmy's home to a reunion of internees at the Lake Tule internment camp (familiar to us from his drawings). Linda's camera follows Jimmy into Block 4, where he was incarcerated for three and a half years. There is one tiny window, high up and barred. Walls are crumbling; maps to the cracks that seem at once like tributaries and boundaries. The camera pans to a particular confluence that has formed through the faded pencil-written words, inscribed some sixty years previously: *Show me the way to go to home* (sic).

The clear message from Tamsen Courtenay's powerful book *Four Feet Under*, in which she gives thirty homeless people the platform to voice their very human stories, is that the distance between our front door and shop doorway is not as great as we might think: any one of us could be living on the streets, stripped of the dignity that we take for granted. Destitution can arrive in different guises. My father cut himself off from the world about six months before he died. I was thirty-three. We'd had a rollercoaster relationship. An award-winning television producer and director, he was brilliant, funny and loving; during happy times in childhood he reminded me of Danny's dad in Roald Dahl's *Danny the Champion of the World*. He lived, though, in the shadow of depression, the kind that leaves you bloated with despair, unable to get out of bed; he self-medicated with alcohol, a personality-twisting dosage. In the year before his death I took time out, unable to empathise any longer with his drinking or its ramifications.

He always said that if he ever got really ill, he'd sail a boat out to sea and not come back. And that is what he metaphorically did … having had cancer of the sinus twice before, the symptoms third time round would have been identifiable and the prognosis a simple equation. In choosing not to tell anyone of his illness, and to be alone, he deprived himself not only of medical support but also of comfort and love, including that from his daughters. (For had I known, my anger would have evaporated, and I would have been at his side.)

A day or so after he had been found, Emily and I were adrift in his Cardiff home. I noted dusty pictures and photographs on the wall that were particularly dear to him; the windows that we had cleaned many a time with newspaper and vinegar; the garden pond he built; I saw him standing there, hand on hip, mug of tea in the other – we'd broken off from a DIY job he'd roped us into – and were chatting about some philosophical conundrum, with Radio 4 playing in the background as always; I heard his roar of laughter, and I could not absorb the horror of what was actually in front of us: the mounds of rubbish and newspaper; empty cans of dog food; the mouse droppings in his precious camera equipment; his blood-soaked mattress. It was as if a homeless person had died in his house. His home had become a building that barely sheltered the fragments of his fragile self; he had lain there confronting death, cold and alone, with memories and demons dripping through the roof.

Once or twice a term my Korean students invited me to dinners at their house shares. In the hallway there would be a library of shoes; as I took mine off, I would be given a pair of sliders to wear. Sometimes eight students might be sharing a room, the windows would be steamed up and we'd perch wherever we could eat, with plates on our laps, wonderful and elaborate suppers of homemade Korean food, including of course, kimchi. They brought the essence of their home in South Korea to me. In turn, this wonderful first class of mine inspired my teaching ethos: that first and foremost everyone should feel at home in my classroom. Shy and introverted, I'm probably not the best guest to invite to your party. For some reason, the classroom was different. I was happy creating an ambience where a class of twenty or so students – with an age range of sixteen to seventy (that at a later job included a Japanese rap artist, a Polish professor of agriculture, a Columbian kite flyer, a Thai hairdresser, a Korean nun) – all felt comfortable.

Home in all its forms involves a journey, and whether it exists or whether it's a shimmering rainbow of a house, entirely unreachable, the quest to be at home is indeed, as Baldwin put it, *an irrevocable condition*.

Chapter Five

A compromise is reached: I don't have to go back to HDU, and I am moved to the unisex observation ward on 4 South. Most of all, I'm relieved to be escaping Faith. The porter edges my bed through the doorway into the smaller ward; ahead is an expanse of bleached sky, framed within the window that stretches the length of the facing wall.

'Bloody hell! Bleedin' agony. It's agony. You sure you've given me morphine? Cos it's not made a jot of difference.' The writhing woman's blue and bloodshot eyes find mine as my bed reaches its destination, the corner space next to hers. Strands of light brown hair squiggle a signature across her perspiring forehead, but that's all I see, my heart is pounding again – at the thought of another Faith – and I heave an inward sigh of relief as the porter draws the cubicle curtains on his way out. A nurse checks the IV stand, and plugs in the mattress. All my belongings have been transferred to the tall wooden cabinet that sits between the bed and the long window; my mother stands on tiptoe to arrange the orchid and cards. The change of scene hasn't affected my sickness and she is kept busy emptying the bowl, replacing it every three vomits, passing me tissues, and reassuring me in the moments when I lie back, clammily spent. In the longer gaps, I close my eyes and she sits in the blue chair on my right-hand side, doing the crossword.

'Okay ... Let's see ... Four down. Golf course hazard. In six. Blank blank N blank blank blank. Don't know anything about golf.'

I open my eyes and watch the cubicle curtain twitching and bulging above her head. Movement next door.

'And it's N because of the large-billed bird, which is definitely TOUCAN.'

My brain is too fuzzy.

'Oh I know, it's … BUNKER!' The same triumph echoes in her voice as when she beats me at Scrabble, or Backgammon. She's competitive, my mother, and I smile now because she still wants to beat me, even in here. But the letters b - u - n - k - e - r stand spindly as winter trees on a green hill; I grasp an image of bunk beds and then toss it away; I hold for longer a wartime shelter crammed with fearful eyes, before blinking that one away too. Can't find golf bunker.

'Let me open the curtains now, I don't want to think of you all closed off,' my mother says at about seven, preparing to leave; checking that my phone, drink, sick bowl and tissues are all within easy reach.

'No. Please don't.' I need everything shut out.

'Okay, okay.'

She kisses me on the forehead, and I thank her for all that she's done today.

She disappears through the curtains, handbag weighing down her left shoulder, newspaper tucked under her arm. I worry about her driving home. She'd never say, but I know she's exhausted. It's like she never admits to being in pain – which she is most of the time, thanks to arthritis. 'It's my Christian Science upbringing,' she'll say in explanation.

It was the upbringing that allowed her to dance on a broken hip at the age of ten, following a fall from a climbing frame. 'If we think positively, Eleanor, the pain will go away,' she was told. Months later, when the pain hadn't gone away, and her right leg dragged behind her, and her place at the Royal Ballet School had been given to another child, my mother was elastoplasted to a traction device, weighted down by bricks, on an adult's orthopaedic ward in Hillend Hospital, a wing of St Bartholomew's that doubled as a psychiatric unit – or 'lunatic asylum' according to Grandma – with visits from her mother allowed only twice a week. Fresh air was a must and the windows were permanently open; my mother lay in terror that the swooping, circling bats would get caught up in her hair.

Every Friday all patients were wheeled into 'The Cinema', a high-ceilinged room where a film would be projected; she found it difficult to concentrate on the antics of Gary Cooper, Gene Kelly and Debbie Reynolds with the comings and goings of the psychiatric patients, who were free to wander around the beds and wheelchairs, *looming like ghosts.*

The traction didn't work and her hip was pinned, which necessitated a further seven months at Hillend. Two other children joined my mother on the ward: four-year-old John, who sang

Catch a falling star an' put it in your pocket
Never let it fade away
Catch a falling star an' put it in your pocket
Save it for a rainy day

repeating the verse over and over, long into the darkness of each night; and fifteen-year-old Celia. Celia was the most mobile out of the three and organised their escapes from the governess who was sent to teach them. She wheeled my mother, and then John, into a broom cupboard, and there the three of them would remain all afternoon, or until a kindly nurse knocked to give them the all-clear. It can't have actually been a broom cupboard, because their hidey-hole had windows, and a table where they could read and play games, but that's what they liked to call it.

'The pins will need to come out in four or five years,' my mother's parents were advised. And Grandma believed that positive thinking would remove that need too. My mother was twenty-eight when X-rays revealed that the pins had rusted through the joint, and they were then removed. This time it was only two weeks in hospital; I was six and screamed my way down the corridor when visiting hours were over, seasick from divorce upheavals the previous year.

Mummy's staring at the sugar bowl, the way she does every breakfast time. It's a magical bowl, like a sparkling mirror ... you can see everything in it, the teapot, my fingers if I wave them up and down, and even stripes of blue sky, and I wonder whether it's like the bath tap that squidges my nose out into a fat triangle, when I'm practising swimming and get right up close. Breakfast is different this morning, Emily's not splatting everything with yoghurt. Her highchair is empty. And Daddy's not here either, Mummy says they stayed the night at Nom's. My toast is cut into soldiers. Some soldiers are thin but the sergeant major has been eating lots of cake. Some are frowning and others are smiling, Mummy dipped the point of her knife into Marmite and drew their small faces, arms, legs and buttons of their uniform. I don't like to bite off their heads so I start with their feet. *Nibble slowly, like a little mouse, Daddy says, that's right, keep your lips together while you chew.* I test how long I can keep my lips together as I think of a cow munching grass.

'Please may I get down, Mummy?' I ask, now the soldiers have become crumbs.

'Mummy?' Her eyes leave the magic bowl.

'Of course, Darling. In fact, it's almost time for us to leave. Now, do you remember what I said?'

'Yes, you said I must choose *one* toy and *one* book to take with me in the car.'

'Good girl. Go and brush your teeth and then get choosing.' Mummy starts clearing the table and I slide off the wooden banquette.

Upstairs, I skate across the shiny cork-tiled floor of my bedroom, easy-peasy in socks. If you cut a 50p coin in half, that would be the shape of my room, the slanted edges are the windows. And in front of the windows there's a big chair, and next to it is a little wicker chair with a red cushion. This is where I play Snap! with Nom. And lying on the table, at the side of her chair, is the pack of cards and the book we've been reading together, *Gobbolino, the Witch's Cat*. On Halloween, I was allowed to stay up late and we sat here witch-watching with hot chocolate for a special treat. It was so dark outside that it was difficult to spot their black capes and pointy hats against the sky. But every so often Nom sucked her teeth and pointed upwards towards a cluster of stars, *Oh my word Harriet*, she'd say, *did you see her … Did you see the size of the cat riding on the back of that broomstick? … Goodness knows how the witch can fly, carrying that tiger's weight*. And Nom would shake her head in disbelief. I got her to open a window and I could barely breathe, she held me so tightly round the waist, as I had a proper look out into the darkness; I could smell the cold night sky and I watched the stars flicker and twinkle at the man in the moon, and I felt a strange gust against my cheek, and thought I heard a distant cackling, but I didn't spot any witches. I felt cosy and safe in the warmth of my room when Nom closed the windows, and we had one more game of cards and one more chapter of *Gobbolino*. Then she helped me get ready for bed, snuggled me down, kissed me goodnight, and switched off the yellow light.

'Darling, why are you crying?' Mummy comes over to where I'm sitting in the wicker chair, holding *Gobbolino*.

'I don't know which toy to take with me,' I say, biting my lip at the lie. I had already decided to take my glove puppet mouse, Jerry. I don't want to hurt Mummy's feelings and tell her that I already miss Daddy, Emily and Nom and our dogs. Don't want to ask *why* we need to leave them. *It's very sad,* she'd said, *but Mummy and Daddy have to separate, we are not going to live together anymore.*

Twelve years ago, when my mother was fifty, her hip was finally replaced.

*

'The whole point of being on this observation ward is to be observed,' says a male nurse. I recognise him as the charge nurse who rectified my deflated bed. He opens the curtains despite my groans, and I'm confronted with a long grey-bearded man in the bed opposite. His visitors smile at me, as I'm revealed – clutching the sick bowl. Who is on the stage, them or me?

'There you are. Can't go hiding yourself away like that,' says the woman next to me, 'we're in the same boat, we are.' I still fear that she's Faith in disguise.

'It's working now. The morphine. I'm trippin' out! I'm trippin' right out. I can see all sorts … I'm high as a bloody kite. Thank God that pain's flown away. It wouldn't do for Bert to see me hollering like that.' She smooths down her hair as if tidying herself for his visit. 'What's your name, Darlin'? I'm Elsa.'

I manage to say my name before throwing up again.

Wide-awake through the night, I hear Faith's crutches clunking past the nurses' station. Can I? I close my eyes; her blackened stare seeps out of the red and orange brickwork.

My muscles continue to work as one, convulsing, conspiring

to be rid of I don't know what, there is nothing left inside me. Mid-retch, electric pain shoots up my body as I involuntarily lean forward; my eyes stream and bulge, I'm a cartoon character, and my eyeballs shall surely pop out – like the acupuncture needles – slippery blue marbles that will roll out of here. In between bouts, I focus on deep breaths, and cracks in the wall's paintwork that become veiny rivers running through imagined countries.

*

Water is milkshake-thick and tastes metallic, tap or bottled. I develop a maddening, itchy craving for ginger ale, a drink I've never liked. Simon, my mother's partner, arrives straight from Snaresbrook Crown Court.

'Here you are, dear. Your mother told me you'd fancy some of this.' He pulls out a bottle from his beat-up briefcase. Small sips. The dryness and the bubbles barge gloriously through the thickness in my mouth. I can never imagine Simon thin. His weight is about his love of food and cooking rather than greed; his girth a testament to stock-splashed recipes of Julia Child's *Mastering the Art of French Cookery Vol. 1*, Escoffier, Elizabeth David and Delia; a metaphor that breathes his generosity. Today he's dapper in a birds-eye suit, shirt collar starched; the vermilion enamel cufflinks I gave him for Christmas are lodged in frayed cuffs – the only reference to his cosy, moth-holed jerseys that my mother is forever trying to lose. Bump into Simon in the street at the weekend and not in a million years would you guess him to be His Honour Judge Wilkinson. His humbleness is one of the things I love about him, none of the arrogance that adorns his profession.

'How are you feeling, dear? Any better?' Simon asks, pulling the chair that my mother has found him closer to the end of my bed. But not too close.

'Much better,' I say with a bright smile, and thank him for the ginger ale.

I close my eyes and listen to him answer my mother's questions about his day in court. It's safe to doze when I have visitors, the gargoyles make themselves scarce.

*

The ward has six beds: three on one side and three on the other. Every four hours Mr Mohammed, opposite me, draws his cubicle curtains. They don't meet entirely, and through the crack I can just see his stilted movements as he bends to roll out a red and brown tasselled mat from under his bed for prayers. Most of the time he sits in his chair, glasses perched on the end of his nose, reading one of the thick maroon-covered volumes on his bedside table. When Mrs Mohammed arrives, his dignified features split into warmth and light, a smile that meets his eyes, as she kisses the top of his bald, domed head. Out of her bag come Tupperware containers filled with homemade samosas, rice dishes and pastries, a tablecloth and cutlery. She sets his bedside table and they eat together. At first Mr Mohammed barely acknowledged me; a couple of days later he calls for a nurse if he sees I am incapacitated. And whenever he passes my bed in his camel dressing gown, IV in tow, he enquires, 'Alright, Toots?' with gentleness in his eyes. Mr Mohammed has an aura that calms my racing mind and helps keep me in the moment.

Elsa speaks at 100mph and at a billion decibels – a machine is brought periodically to her bedside that monitors circulation in her right leg. The mighty gales and crashing waves are the sounds of Elsa's blood. Her slender feet and elegantly painted toenails underline her pain-worn face. Bert, her husband, visits every evening. I'm a magpie, their conversations glitter with a closeness that is exotic within these pale blue walls.

'Got me nighties?' she asks.

'Now I'm not gonna forget them am I, Elsa? How's the pain today?'

'I'm flyin' on the morphine! Circulation's up the spout but hey ho. Franklyn says if they can't clear the blood path, they're gonna saw it off. No, Bert ... don't look like that. It'll save me on nail polish. How are the dogs, you giving Bella her biscuits separately?'

'Yeah, yeah ... of course. What you worrying about that for? They were making a right din in the garden this morning, told them to put a sock in it ... sorted 'em out with a walk good enough.'

'What? Up the park? Don't you go tiring yourself out. It'll be all we bleedin' need if both of us go down.'

'Nipped into the pub on my way home last night. Saw Maureen. She sends her best.'

'Still dillying with Old Handsome, is she?'

'Dunno, she didn't mention him, and I've not seen him this week. But she's done something funny with her hair.'

'Funny *how*?' Increased decibels.

'Well, it's the colour. It's gone orange. Really. She's that scrawny that she looks like a lit-up Belisha beacon ... come to think of it, she was wearing black and white too. Praps she was on her way to a fancy dress party.'

'Must've been bleedin' fluorescent for you to have noticed, Bert! When do you ever notice stuff like hair?'

'Sylvie's coming up the hospital on Saturday.'

'Is she gonna bring the baby? Dunno how that girl does it.' Elsa turns sideways to me and raises her eyebrows. 'Four rugrats, and that job, and no bleedin' husband, I ask you!' Just as I begin to worry that she wants my input to the conversation, she reaches for her newspaper.

*

The vampire, a young, slight Chinese phlebotomist, slips into the observation ward every morning at 6.30 a.m. He doesn't turn on lights, and moves quietly around the beds, taking vials of our dark red blood.

'Good morning,' he says in just above a whisper, with a quick smile, and with an intimacy that suggests each of his victim's blood is the most sacred of all. He tightens the blue rubber tourniquet, and very gently traces the dip that is the inside of my elbow with his fingertips. 'Sharp scratch,' he says softly, and each time the needle goes in, I think of cats' claws, rose thorns, and the scraps Emily and I had as children. Of course, I do not look forward to having my blood taken, but his presence each morning is oddly comforting, and it signals the end of clock-watching the night away.

No food. The kitchen smells remain rank. And everyone – nurse, doctor, visitor – who comes near me reeks of sulphur. How can everyone smell of the same eggy stench? It is most probably me stinking.

'Excuse me, would it be possible to have some more tissues?' my mother asks the nurse who has just finished tending to Elsa, and she gestures to an empty box and to the remnants of a voluminous puking session.

'No. No more. I'm afraid you've used up your quota.' The nurse barely gives us a second glance before she marches out of the ward.

'Oh my gawd, did I hear that right?' says Elsa.

'Won't be long,' my mother says and disappears in hot pursuit.

Of course, it is not a problem for her to bring me in boxes of tissues from home, she brings in everything she possibly can to make me more comfortable. As the nausea surges again, I'm confused. Does the nurse think I'm vomiting on demand, in order to waste tissues? My mother returns with a new box.

'I suggested that a little kindness wouldn't go amiss,' she says, handing me a couple of the new tissues just in time.

'Crikey, I would've suggested a lot more than that!' I hear Elsa say as I bury as much of my head as I can into the cardboard bowl.

Mr Mohammed, Elsa and I make an unlikely threesome: our paths almost certainly would not have crossed in our day-to-day lives, yet we have only been in each other's company for a few days in this surreal setting and a bond has developed. The artist Slinkachu leaps from a shelf in my mind to remind me of his photographs of miniature railway-set figurines. He flicks through his portfolio and stops at *They're Not Pets*. A man points a rifle at a bee that looks dead, the bee is lying on its side and with its wing vertically extended; it is the same height as the man, but dwarfs the man's small daughter standing by his side clutching a teddy. Slinkachu photographed the scene twice, once from a standing position so all you see is a section of random pavement, albeit sun-speckled, and the little people are invisible; for the main shot he is down on his knees for a close-up, and the bee is a gigantic beast. His photographs are *Gulliver's Travels* and *Alice in Wonderlandish* all at once; he makes a nonsense out of perspective, and it *is* as if Mr Mohammed, Elsa and I have each fallen down a rabbit hole, or perhaps whirled up a plughole, and landed on the observation ward as little people.

'Oi! Mr Mohammed, how do you like being on a mixed ward?' Elsa calls across one morning after our ablutions.

I hold my breath.

Mr Mohammed looks up from his book that he'd just picked up, and thinks for a moment.

'It's colourful Elsa, isn't it? And my wife tells me that I'm fortunate to be in the presence of two such strong individuals. My wife is always right about such things. And you? What are your thoughts?'

'Well, it'd be nice to have a bit of old Daniel Craig opposite, don't ya think Harriet? And *which bit* could be up for a debate. Nah, seriously Mr M., you might not have his brawn, but you're alright. And I only asked cos I was thinking that it was strange how it doesn't bother me, you on the ward, being a man and all that ... and then I wondered what it felt like in your boots, cos of you know ... religion and whatnot.'

'The best religion is understanding others, and treating others – no matter how different – as you'd want to be treated. That's the way I see it. At the end of the day, we've been put here together, and Allah willing we can help each other in some tiny way. Don't you agree, Toots?' he says, looking in my direction.

I nod.

'Yes, well I think we can count our lucky stars that we got ourselves a sage. Daniel who?' says Elsa.

*

Fork lightning and flashing pinhead lights shimmer across the ward, settling like raindrops dripping down a window.

'You alright, Toots?'

'Migraine,' I say, shading my eyes, and buzzing for a nurse.

'You'll be waiting all day, my dear. Let me go and find someone for you.'

Mr Mohammed gets up from his chair and shuffles past me with his IV in tow.

'Bloody 'ell, Darlin! That's all you need, that is!' says Elsa.

'You have headache? Right?' asks the Filipino nurse who has accompanied Mr Mohammed back to my bedside.

'Migraine aura,' I say.

'What order?' Her nose is missing and a crescent is shimmering on her right cheek.

'No, aura ... my vision.' It's difficult to find my words.

'You cannot *see*?!'

'Do you have *Migraleve*?' I say, headache queuing.

'You can't see, I get doctor.'

'No doctor, just tablets,' I say, but the nurse has already disappeared.

Elsa thinks this is out of *The Two Ronnies*, she's laughing so hard.

'Oh mate! ... You didn't get your order in!'

'Laughter's the best medicine, eh Toots?' says Mr Mohammed, reading my mind. About half an hour later, my vision has returned and I get a couple of paracetamol for the headache. The Pain Team is constantly on my case for not taking their concoctions; nausea and migraine are small fry.

'Them lights don't help your head, do they?' Elsa points to the strip lighting above.

'Not really.'

'Cos my mother suffered with migraines, and it was the sun, would you believe, that brought them on.'

'Well, it's perfectly light in here, isn't it Elsa ... we don't need the main lights on, do we?'

'Course not, Mr M. Now that's what you call service, isn't it, Harriet?' says Elsa as Mr Mohammed turns the lights off at the main switch by the door. When Maria, the same Filipino nurse as earlier, comes in to give Mr Mohammed some medicine, she switches them back on, and this time it's Elsa that struggles over and turns the lights off. A couple of hours later and a passing nurse comes in and flicks the switch, 'Lights!' Mr Mohammed and Elsa shout in unison, but she doesn't hear. Mr Mohammed goes off for a chat with the nurses' station. They agree that bedside lights will suffice unless there is an emergency.

*

It isn't just the three of us all the time. Late one evening a young man is admitted to the bed next to Mr Mohammed, opposite Elsa. He's out of surgery from having his leg amputated. I watch two nurses do their best to make him comfortable. He doesn't want the sheet covering him. The stump is bandaged, neatly unnatural. It's 2 a.m. and the man is staring at me from under his afro. I look away. Shut my eyes. Open them again, and his gaze is unwavering. When I close my eyes again, the red-brick wall is waiting for me once more; it crumbles and I am face-to-face with leery grimaces. So I busy myself with sipping ginger ale and other nocturnal activities. There is actually much to distract me: studying the wall for unexplored cracks, hiking their crevices as if I were inching along the skimpy planks that edge Mount Hua, but every time I look back, the man is still staring at me.

Over the next couple of days he vents his anger on the nurses, first by shouting and then by hitting them. Events culminate and my mother is hardly through the doorway on her afternoon visit before Elsa fills her in.

'Can you smell it, Elly? Can you smell it?'

My mother puts her handbag down on the bed and looks around. 'Yes, what is *that* smell?'

'I'm not sure you really want to know,' says Mr Mohammed from his chair.

'Course she wants to know. Well it was him, see he's gone.' Elsa gesticulates towards the stripped bed opposite. Decibel level is high.

'The nurses had just cleaned him up, like. Then what does he do? He shits himself again, on purpose ... and then ...'

'Elsa!' Mr Mohammed interrupts in vain.

'Well she's gotta know, she's gotta know what's been goin on … Yeah, so he dirtied himself and THEN he smears it all over the next nurse, like it was paint, and when another nurse comes to help, he HITS them and covers them both with his shit. That's what the bleedin' smell is, I'm telling you.'

My mother looks over to me and I nod, faint from vomiting.

'And that was after he'd flung his IV at me, he did, didn't he?' Elsa looks at me and Mr Mohammed for confirmation. 'It missed me by inches it did.'

'Yes he did,' Mr Mohammed says to my mother. 'I'm not sure I'd have been brave enough to take Elsa on like that.'

'Bert phoned me this morning, which he never does cos he hates phones. And you know what? He came late last night, cos he had to sort out one of his daughters, well, he said that he had to see if we were ALRIGHT, cos evidently when he went home there was a police guard standing outside the ward! It's a bleedin' disgrace, ANYTHING could've happened to us!'

My mother is duly horrified and has a hundred questions for Elsa, who is delighted to be able to go into further details. Mr Mohammed raises his eyebrows at me and returns to his book.

*

Ward round. It seems to be a new team of doctors every day. In spite of their various faces, they all stand at the end of my bed in the same tulip-stemmed way. They might ask how I am; apart from that, I am not involved in their discussions. Today is different. The suave registrar takes the lead.

'Harriet, we know about the nausea, but do you have any pain?' he asks with a smile.

'Whenever I move.'

'What kind of pain is it?'

'Up, down, like an electric shock.'

'So pretty fierce, then?'

'Mmm.' I know where this is going; he could be a barrister.

'Well, can you explain why you're not using the pump, provided by The Pain Team?'

'Don't like my mind feeling fuzzy,' I'm not comfortable with telling them about the gargoyles, 'and don't want anything that makes the nausea worse.'

'The thing is Harriet, once this nausea's under control we'll start your physio again. And in order for that to happen we need to manage your pain.'

'Why won't the sickness stop?'

'Well, we think it's the haematoma squashing your stomach. We just have to wait for it to start reducing in size.'

'How long?'

'Yours is a condition we can only observe and manage, there are so few cases to refer to ... with the Angiomyolipoma being as substantial as yours.'

There's not much I can say to that, even if I had the energy.

'So will you use the pump?'

My answer is noncommittal, and I remember a visit to the dentist as a child when it was discovered I needed a filling. I refused the injection; no amount of cajoling from my mother or the dentist would persuade me. The drilling was brutal. But there had been no way that I wanted to feel *numb*.

Some while later, one of the doctors in the entourage comes by. Dr Flower. She could not be more appropriately named. She does not smell of sulphur. She pulls the curtains round my bed.

'May I sit down?' Her voice is kind.

'We've got an alternative to the pump,' she says, presenting what looks like an Elastoplast sealed in a blistered pack. 'It's a

Fentanyl patch, and you keep it on for three days and then it gets replaced.'

'But it has side effects?'

'Well, because it's a patch, the drug's release is that much more gradual and you really shouldn't feel any. And Harriet, every drug, even over-the-counter drugs and simple antibiotics, carry long lists of possible side effects.'

'I'm tired. Tired of being sick.'

'I understand, but we really do need to address the pain as well.'

'Okay,' I say, too weary to argue. She's right. I need physio. I need to get moving. I shouldn't be here. I don't want to be here. I want to be home.

Dr Flower takes the patch out and presses it gently onto the back of my ribcage.

'It'll take a day or so for it to start working, and if you do feel peculiar or if you think it's increasing the nausea, we'll take it off.'

You're a pushover, Harriet, I tell myself.

*

Night-time. It's like a whole new day. Eight and a half hours to fill.

The cannula is suddenly loose. *Can it come out, now I haven't got the pain pump?* Apparently not. A floppy-haired House Doctor tiptoes in to replace it; *make a fist,* he whispers amid much tapping of the back of my hand, *just feeling for a vein ... hmmm ... they seem to be hiding, so flex your fingers for me ... that's right ... ah got one, sharp scratch* and blood spurts over the pillow upon which my hand is resting. The vein has collapsed. He repeats the process three times; no gloves, nicotine drills my nostrils with his every hand movement. My hand is sore, my gown bloodied. *Okay, sorry about this, but I'm going to have to get someone else to do this for you.* Dr Flower arrives: *Let's give that hand a rest, shall we?* And she pops the cannula into the back of my right hand.

Back to clock-distracting nocturnal activities.

Yesterday, I had a new craving, which Simon indulged: fresh pineapple, the only food I've eaten since the Cup-a-Soup on HDU. There are a few chunks left. I let the juice trickle down my throat as slowly as I can. My palate is belly-dancing to its sweet tune.

Mr Mohammed stirs. *Still awake, Toots?* he asks before slipping into dream. His voice has warmed the night.

I try a new sleep-inducing tactic of breathing in time with Mr Mohammed's sleeping form, and then to Elsa's snoring rhythm.

*

'Um … we've got a surprise for you,' Emily says. I detect an anxious tone. 'It's Amelia. She's come to visit you … would you like to see her?'

'Amelia?'

'Yes, Amelia.'

'Haven't seen her for so long.'

'I know,' Emily takes my hand, 'but she's here now.'

A couple of years ago we had a nuclear fall-out, one of those incidents that is wired with pettiness from both sides. But now, viewed from my hospital bed, it is minute against the panorama of friendship that preceded it.

Emily and my mother bring her to my bedside, my sister's eyes are full of tears. *We'll leave you to it,* she says. Any bad feeling has evaporated and I'm shaking inside with happiness to see her. Our eyes lock. Joy in Amelia's face; almost instantaneously it evaporates, her smile is forced unnaturally wide by her eyes, which have rounded with horror: her shock becomes my shock.

It dawns on me that I am accustomed to my family's faces, that they only show me positivity in their expressions. Anders said I didn't look *half as bad* as he thought I was going to look. Yet this is Amelia, who from the age of eighteen has travelled the world on her own, who knows the Middle East like the back of her hand, who is consulted by the BBC World Service on what life is like in those war-torn regions: she knows *real* life. *And she is shocked by the sight of me.* I am desperate to make her feel better, to take away that shock. A flash of turquoise and crimson, and I remember the cover of the book I had just started before this all began, that my mother brought in for when I feel like reading again. I point up to the top of the cabinet, to leopard-face orchid, and to the 1,000-plus-page brick, *Shantaram*. She reaches up for it.

'Take it.'

'Oh no, I couldn't, you must read it,' she says, flicking through its pages.

'I will … after you.'

Amelia squeezes my fingers. When we say goodbye, she is in tears.

'You will be all right, won't you, Sweetie?' she asks, childlike, her expression so far removed from its normal confident countenance.

'Yes, of course,' I say.

I am terrified by Amelia's fear. I cannot get her shocked face out of my mind.

Fear on Saturday morning: Fear is summoning the strength to wash. Fear is black spots in front of my eyes as I struggle to lean forward. Fear is almost passing out as a nurse helps me move to the blue chair next to my bed. Fear is sitting in that chair with a nosebleed and with *The Guardian* on my bedside table, not having the strength to pick it up or having the concentration span to read a headline. Fear is indignity. Fear is feeling that I'm taking backward steps. Fear is realising that I haven't eaten anything more solid than a pineapple chunk for three weeks. Fear is being properly scared by this weakness for the first time, worrying whether this is it.

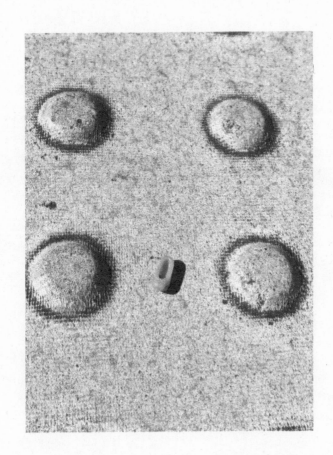

Chapter Six

Sunset in Singledom

'I guess colour. Especially green. Light. Certain smells ... like oil paint, wet woodland, river ...' I replied when Fernando had asked through quick sips of coffee what turned me on. We were on a first date. *Right*, he had said, reaching for the sugar pot, in a tone that suggested both disappointment, and that I was weird. After he stirred in sweetness he began the sipping again, like a tongue-flicking chameleon. I had yet to forgive him for not having a Spanish accent, and for the eight-inch lie.

Once upon a time I took it very much for granted that I'd get married, and have my own happily-ever-after family. It never occurred to me that I would find myself in middle age childless and exiled to Singledom, gazing out to sea – in the shadow of What Might Have Been – bearing an uncanny resemblance to Edvard Munch's woodcut, *Two Women on the Shore*. A postcard print of the image is in my left hand: a young woman with long red hair stands on the shore looking out to the setting sun, its reflection in the sea is columnar and phallic; the blues and greens of land, sea and sky are blissfully muted – I could well live within this palate. It's a calming picture. Until I move my thumb, to reveal the macabre woman shrouded in black with a skeleton's face. She's sitting behind the young woman, so deathly close it's as if her black weeds are stitched to the white silk of her young self's dress – the seam evoking the harshness with which age can overtake youth. The mood is very much of loneliness and of time lost.

Considering my yearning to have children, I was profligate with time. I stuck with a love for twelve years, convinced that I would change his mind about commitment and babies. Such woeful arrogance, on my part. It was a wonderful, enriching relationship in many other respects; it just took me down a path that headed in the opposite direction of that particular dream. (He has, though, since become my best friend.) After my illness there was another relationship that lasted four years, and brought the dream within a millimetre of my fingertips: I became pregnant, and miscarried; a year later he proposed, the dress and venue were sorted; events conspired, and we parted. The loss of pregnancy and break-up clenched a fist that threw a knockout blow to my temple.

It was Minakshi, a dear school friend, senior policy advisor to a government think tank and mother of four-year-old twin boys, who pressed me to have a go at online dating. *Honestly Harriet, everyone's doing it. My colleague Elena has met such nice guys. Really nice. She's been dating one of them for quite a while. What've you got to lose?* And Mini was right. It was three years since the-marriage-that-never-happened. I had little control over my aspirations for motherhood but perhaps I might dare to share again. And so I gathered up my preconceptions of stigma and desperation, chucked them in the skip on top of the broken panes of memory, swiped past Tinder, and filled out a couple of profile questionnaires; albeit with a half-hearted nib, chewing the pen top over questions surrounding my occupation ... *what exactly are you, Ms Under Achiever? Photographer, English language teacher, or sales assistant? All three.* Boxes of interest:

music □
literature □
art □
photography □
cinema □
theatre □
travel □
nature □
walking □

I resisted snipping several years off my age, and posted current photos of myself, one of them with whippet.

*

Fernando was the fourth date. The first had been a doctor whose curls clipped the grubby collar of his white shirt like pubic hairs clinging to a grimy bath, while his jumper had hummed of naphthalene. The second was an architect who spent the duration of dinner telling me about the number of people he employed and how much he paid each of them, and about his ex-wife. She lived in the same apartment block as him, *I mean she's ten years older than me, about to get her Freedom Pass, and she dates guys in their **thirties**! She's **so** hot!* His exclamation marks were voluble. The third professed to be a member of some specialist terror squad in the police, *I'm the fastest at putting on the biochemical protective suit and gas mask in a timed drill*; he was, it turned out, a deskbound constable, who didn't even have to wear uniform, where was the fun in that?

Fingers crossed for Fernando, read Mini's text that morning. Her optimism had been contagious, and I viewed the Spaniard in my supermarket trolley as if he were a prize Andalusian cherimoya: my very own Bardem-Almodóvar-Lorca-Pla-Sorolla-Nadal rolled into one delicious fruit. He lived in Battersea, wanted to meet in Richmond, and as we had both ticked *Travel* in *Interests*, it seemed fun to bump into one another in the Travel section of Waterstone's. I arrived on the second floor early, crossed the homely creaking floorboards to the armchair in the window alcove, and sat listening to the heave of buses lurching round the corner; watching people come up the stairs, *Is that him? The guy with the stubble?* Nope. He'd headed over to Plays. *Pity.* Nerves fully carbonated – *Do I look okay? ... Is the jumper too casual?... Did I remember to put on mascara?* I creaked back over to the Travel shelves and browsed epic journeys, before my glance flitted to Scandinavia, primarily Sweden, and then Asia.

'Hey. Are you Harriet?' I was lost in Burma and hadn't heard the footsteps. 'Fernando?' I said, swinging round, forgetting the oh-so-casual *Hola* I'd rehearsed in the bath that morning. He sounded nothing like the imaginary Fernando. Nor did he resemble the online profile Fernando. His crown met my shoulders before he went on tiptoes to greet me with a kiss – exactly at the same time that I stuck out my hand for him to shake. If he was 5'll, then I've been 6'3 all these years, not 5'6. My former fiancé was a couple of inches shorter than me and for four years he was the tallest person in any room, so it's not as if I was height prejudiced. It was more my date's need to strut his profile in platform boots that led me to sense it an inauspicious start to our afternoon, in spite of the glorious sunshine.

On the way to the café we walked along the towpath, passing under Richmond Bridge and Rapunzel tresses of weeping willows, and crossed Petersham Meadow. *Hope it doesn't get too muddy, I gave them an extra polish especially for you,* he said, pointing down to a shiny pair of brogues, the exact same shade of brown as his leather bomber jacket. I was tempted to remind him that the walk, *whatever the weather*, had been his idea, but restrained from doing so. Besides, we were on the same page as far as our choice of jeans and I was determined to proceed with an open mind, to be more tolerant: I tried hard to ignore the cloying waft of cologne, and his habit of stepping directly, repeatedly into my walkway; it was more difficult to empathise with the veer of his conversation.

'So, have you been dating online long?' he asked.

'A couple of months. And you?'

'Yeah. Six months. Not finding it terribly satisfactory.'

'No?'

'I end up with dates who've lied on their profiles ... you know, profile pics that were a passing likeness ... what, ten years ago? I walked out on one. It was the classic scene of disappearing out the back of the restaurant. Because she'd really piled on the pounds, you know, since her profile pic ... yours is *up-to-date*, I'm pleased to say,' he said as if he were putting a medal round my neck, with lingering fingers, oblivious to any hypocrisy. I ignored the pun and enquired instead after his young children.

'They're not much fun. Always whining. Which makes me kind of resentful, you know. When you earn 150 grand a year, it'd be cool to spend six months travelling instead of seeing it all disappear on their school fees, and what thanks do you get? Nothing from them, or from the ex-wife, of course.' Once at the café, the conversation dived a few fathoms deeper, and after an hour and a half of listening I made my excuses and left; *I should at least get a kiss on the lips*, he opined before following up with a long and recriminatory text. 'That was the last one. Back to organic,' I said to Mini in our post-mortem. Either I was too picky, or spectacularly illiterate in reading between the lines of dating profiles. Perhaps both.

Shortly after my date with Fernando, I was leaning over the railings at Southbank: the drawn-out tide had left the river with the skinniest, cinched waist. And in the gloaming the beach was metallic; its light magnetic, pulling me down wrought-iron steps until I was sinking into sand. A breeze kicked up, waffles and burgers on its sweet-sour breath; the Thames catching its coat tails, smelling more like the sea than earthy river. Camera out. Crouched down. Ribcage vibrating – *an echo chamber* – at the percussion of my heart drumming to the beat of *this colour*: to the left was the broken yolk of sun, smeared with scarlet and orange, *a Negroni spilt over the horizon*, silhouetting turrets poking over Waterloo Bridge; to the right, streaks of pink and mauve bruised the spire of St Martin in the Field and the deco angles of Shell Mex House, its clock face lit up, hands nudging 6.15 p.m. Ultraviolet flared down from the bridge's arches, rippling pillars in the currents of the *dirty old river*, and then, refracted, they shimmered across the damp beach, picking out pebbles, shells, pieces of glass, driftwood and beer cans as if the whole scene was an installation. I felt guilty about photographing the sunset. A photograph can never recreate such ephemeral magic. The colours will always be flattened and the secret of the moment lost. But on this occasion I justified the case for indulgence ... *the iridescence* ... *saves it from cliché*, and clicked the shutter twice as The Kinks' 'Waterloo Sunset' played full volume around my mind. Gulls screeched, and the pigtailed little girl coming down the steps with her father, hand in hand, giggled as one swooped close to her cloud of candyfloss. Back up on the promenade, I headed towards Waterloo Station, one eye on the melted horizon, and weaved through the flow of commuters on their way to Blackfriars. *Hey! Darlin'!* A *Big Issue* vendor stepped out in front of me from nowhere, all floppy hair and high cheekbones, his voice jolting me from thoughts of Fernando. I rooted around in my pocket for a couple of quid; the vendor was staring at me. *'Great eyebrows!'* he said at last with a thumbs up. *'Don't shave 'em whatever ya do, Darlin.'* He was off before I could give him the coins, his sack of *Big Issues* slung over his shoulder, while I stood for a moment, laughing hard at the incongruity of his observation, coming right out of the sunset as it did. One thing's for sure: as lonely and freaky as it feels not to have a life partner in crime, I wouldn't want to share moments, like this sunset, with someone for the sake of it. Just as I am unable to capture the sunset's uniquely coalesced colours, I doubt that online dating can manufacture the jigsaw synchronicity of two people meant to be.

Two years later, there was an organic date, with John. Literally a dream date, as that night I had two premonitory dreams. In the first, we were driving and walking through Georgia O'Keefe land in New Mexico that merged blissfully into quintessential English countryside; in the second dream, I was at his side when he suddenly became very ill. The five months we were together was an amazing journey, and we saw beautiful things. I was also with him when he discovered he had cancer, and then when he subsequently passed away. An online dating company would not have matched our profiles in a hundred years. He was ultra-organised, immaculately turned out, jeans pressed; I'm scruffy and scatty. Our karaoke sessions in the car left him groaning with laughter; *and me a chorister, having to put up with this …* he'd say of my singing. *Look at the mess in my kitchen,* he'd sigh, wiping away peelings that had barely hit the work surface. But he also said we fit together like a jigsaw. When he invited me round to his flat for the first time, to play me his vinyl, and to show me a picture of Palmyra, the first thing I saw on his living room wall was the framed lyrics of 'Waterloo Sunset'. I gave him a print of the photograph I took that day and he hung it next to the lyrics. It jolted me again when his children chose it as the final song at the funeral.

*

And just as motherhood is not meant to be, it might be that
Singledom is meant for me.

Chapter Seven

Ward rounds. Seven more doctors, faceless in their anonymity, in a huddled semicircle at the side of my bed; they sway and nod in the breeze of their consultant's eye. I don't recognise him, his black suit a zebra stripe among the white coats. He's flicking through my notes. I wait for him to replace the clipboard before I can read his NHS tag: *Mr Ahmed,* resplendent on a vermillion tie. Mr Ahmed steps forward, and a cloud of Terre d'Hermès blindfolds me, spinning my senses as if I'm a gyroscope. Familiarity hauls me into a bistro on Rue Saint-André-des-Arts, Paris. A Bourgogne-infused hum emanates from lunching locals, the tables are crammed close; through the blur of laden forks meeting mouths, of copper pans and white linen, of mirror silver and glinting glass, I spot Max in the leather-banqueted far corner.

'Unless you start eating, we'll have to put a tube up your nose and into your stomach, and feed you that way. It's not very pleasant,' Mr Ahmed says by way of introducing himself.

His words and tone are not making sense. *Unless I start eating?* Bewildered, my brain jilts Paris and Max, and ransacks its archives, hurling out inked cartoons of suffragettes being forcibly fed, images that were filed over twenty years ago. There I am on my eighteenth birthday at Reading University Library, my fingers smoothing down the violet frayed binding of the WSPU's[41] newspaper *Votes For Women* that I was to trawl through for an A-Level history project.

---

41   WSPU: Women's Social and Political Union

What's the word … collage, no; mirage, no; it is definitely -age though. Got it. Gavage. I focus on one of the drawings now wallpapering my mind: a cell in Holloway Prison, 1910 or thereabouts. A woman on a tilting-backwards chair, being held down by four bony-faced women; there are two doctors dour in black frock coats, one of them steadies her head while the second stands on a chair above her, holding the funnel end of the rubber tubing that has been forced up the suffragette's nose, in his other hand is a clay jug, the contents of which he pours into the funnel.

'Do you understand?' Mr Ahmed is now leaning over me. I nod. No strength to put him right, to remind him that he is not addressing someone on hunger strike; that I have no control over this nausea and lack of appetite, or to tell him that I am scared.

'Good girl.' He gives a flatline smile, and a curt nod to his entourage who follow him out of the ward.

*

Mr Mohammed's glasses have slipped down his nose; he's fallen asleep in his chair, hands clasping one of his weightier books. Elsa has been taken off for tests. Emily has just left to get back to Berkshire in time to collect Alice and Maddy from school. I'm a heavy ball for her to juggle and she must be spending a fortune on petrol and parking, she needn't come to see me every day. A rubbery squeak interrupts guilt, and a porter wheels in a man with a translucent pallor, he has an oxygen cannula and is breathing hard.

'Right, let's get you nice and comfy, Reg,' says the Filipina staff nurse, pulling the cubicle curtains round the bed opposite Elsa.

'Stay safe, mate,' the porter calls over his shoulder as he pushes the empty wheelchair back through the curtains.

'There we are. Right Reg, I'm just going to check your obs … come on, I need to just pop this on your finger to get a reading …'

'Naff off. I don't want foreigners touching me. Where's my wife?' Reg's words are spat in rasping waves.

'Sir, it's for your own good, we need to see how your heart's doing.'

'I said, where's my wife?'

The furious tones coming from behind the curtain have been enough to stir Mr Mohammed. A woman in a beige raincoat hovers in the doorway, carrying a small holdall.

'I'm looking for my husband, Reg,' she says, her eyes teary. I point towards the cubicled bed, the woman smiles and pats down her grey-blond hair. She takes a deep breath before poking her head through the curtains and colliding with the nurse, who leaves looking tight-lipped.

'Oh look what the cat's dragged in.'

'Don't be like that, love, I went home and got everything you asked for. How are you feeling?'

There's a grunt, and then the click of a bedside cabinet being opened and closed, a rustling of newspaper.

'Kath, will you stop fussing, it's doing my head in.'

'I just want to make sure you've got everything to hand, love. Look, I've clipped your glasses over the paper here, and your flannel and sponge bag are in the locker there, and here's your pen for the crossword. Shall I …'

'Don't you ever bloody listen, woman? I don't wanna hear another peep. Don't you think I've got enough on my plate without you wittering on?'

'Oh Reg, that's not fair.'

'*Oh Reg, that's not fair.*' He mimics her with a pantomime dame whine.

'I don't mean to give you the hump, love ... I'm worried about you, can't you see?'

'Quit the snivelling.' The sniffing continues.

Mr Mohammed catches my eye and shakes his head. It's like listening to an afternoon play on the radio; the reality is making me cringe. A different Filipina nurse has appeared with what looks like an ancient IBM computer on a trolley. She pops her head in through the curtains.

'Hello Reg. We're going to wire you up to this heart monitor, I just need to stick these pads on your chest.'

'Right Kath, if you wanna do something really useful, go find me an *English* nurse. And while you're at it, a cuppa wouldn't go amiss.'

'Reg!'

'Oh just get me a cup of tea, will you.' The curtains part and Kath slips out, head bowed. A rhythmic bleeping sets my own heart racing back to Critical Care.

'You're all set up now, Reg.' The nurse pulls back the curtains and departs with a thin smile.

Can this frail-looking white-haired gentleman with sunken cheeks really be that same bully? When Kath returns with the tea, she finds her husband asleep.

Elsa is returned to the ward, wailing. Her cries are raw; pain peeled to the quick. She claws the air with scarlet nails, and with her every cry I feel more helpless. Mr Mohammed shuffles over, his IV in tow.

'Elsa. Shall I get you a nurse?'

'Nah. I've had morphine. It's me leg, the blood's not getting through.' Her eyes are on another planet. Mr Mohammed squeezes her hand and returns to his chair.

An hour passes, before she is calm and staring hard at Reg.

'Where did *he* come from? My Bert would nut me if I created like that,' She says in a loud whisper to my mother, who's just arrived.

'Careful. He'll hear,' my mother whispers back, all mock rebuke.

'And do I care? Nope. Bert walks the dogs, does the laundry, takes two buses to get here every day *and* he's in remission for *his* cancer. It's a lot, you know. Like what you're doing for Harriet. Mrs Mohammed, too. And what *she's* trying to do. Nah. He needs a good slap.'

It's past midnight, and I'm meandering through the day's happenings. Mr Ahmed's face is grimacing at the forefront. *Maybe he made the assumption that I'm choosing not to eat because I refused the anti-sickness meds. They made me doubly nauseous. That's weird ... the bleeping of Reg's monitor has slowed right down; now the alarm's going crazy.*

The fluorescent overhead lighting has gone on. Two nurses sprint to his bedside.

Mr Mohammed is rubbing his eyes.

'Reg, are you okay? Reg, can you hear me?' One of the nurses is leaning over him, looks like she's shining a torch into his eyes.

'Oh gawd! What's going on?' Elsa's awake too.

'Can we get some help in here?' calls the other nurse.

It's only seconds before three more nurses appear with a crash trolley. There's the click of high heels and a woman in an evening gown arrives, a nurse passes her a stethoscope just as another nurse closes first Elsa's and then my cubicle curtains, and then presumably Mr Mohammed's.

'I don't have a pulse. He's not breathing.'

'One at 360, no pulse.'

'And clear!'

The voices bleed into the night, quiet and indistinct.

Fear sidles in, through the crack of my cubicle curtains. His glacial breath steals up my neck and blows gently into my ears.

Skeletal fingers flick through my thoughts as casually as if they were skipping through index cards. Every so often he pulls one out and presses it to the gaping hole of his mouth. I try distracting myself with a sip of ginger ale; the dry sweetness might spark innocuous thoughts. But it's no good; I know what's happened to Reg; *you're so weak you don't even have the strength to read a newspaper's headline, you can't sit up by yourself, and you can't hold a conversation. If it's happened to Reg, it can happen to you. No problem.* The feeling of dread that has prowled my being since childhood is taunting me:

My thoughts about death first waved their podgy arms after a bedtime story on 27 December, my fourth Christmas. In the glow of a nightlight, I lay snug on my side, counting the tiny flowers edging the pale pink Paisley swirls that patterned my eiderdown; I was thinking about the blue-painted nursery school, and how it was big enough, that it would fit everyone in ... that everyone could die together. The chairs that we'd used for Nativity could be pushed back against the walls and everyone could sit there: Mummy, Daddy, Nom, Grandma, my aunts, and all the cousins. We would all sit there together and wait for it to happen, we could hold hands and tell stories, and when it did happen, we would all go to Heaven together, no one would be left lonely or sad.

Die. I tried out my new word a couple more times ... Die. Die. A journey that takes you past the moon and stars. I had learnt it that morning. *Why's the sofa in the garden?* I'd asked. Even though the sofa was flowery, it shouldn't be in the garden; it should be inside, opposite the fireplace. Honda was curled up on one of the arms, she still purred like a motorbike in her sleep. Mummy, big with a baby, had taken my hand and led me back inside.

'Darling … listen, Granny Davy went to Heaven last night … she fell asleep on the sofa and didn't wake up. Poor Nom, she's very sad that Granny's gone.' Great Granny Davy was Nom's mother, and Nom was my father's mother. I didn't understand. Granny Davy never sat on the sofa, she was always on the tall chair with Candy the Pekingese on her lap, and I would sit on the footstool by her side, counting the blue, pink and yellow squares of the crocheted blanket that warmed her knees.

'But why did Granny Davy go to Heaven?'

'Well, when someone is very old … how old was Granny Davy, Harriet?

'Ninety-three,' I say, proud of my numbers.

'Yes, there you are, when someone is very old and tired like Granny Davy was, or if they're terribly ill, there comes a time when they leave this world … and die … and go to Heaven.'

'Mummy, are you going to die?'

'We all die one day, Darling. But hopefully not for a very long time.'

A few weeks later, I'm wearing a pink and purple corduroy pinafore dress, navy woollen tights, and am sitting cross-legged on the floor of my bedroom. I've been doing my favourite book. Doing, because first of all you unfold its cardboard covers and secret flaps, then you bring them together, sliding them into one another so that the book stands up like a merry-go-round with pages instead of painted horses. Long-bearded trolls stroll through the green leaves, on the lookout for a fairy to sweep their caves clean.

There's a buzz, a buzzing. It stops.

Hide up the tree, hide up the tree! I beg the fairy's wings to beat faster – knowing that they won't. The buzzing starts again. I look up, straight into the face of white sun. But the buzzing isn't blinded, on it goes, and it makes me think of when my lips hummed against a comb wrapped in tracing paper and the funny tickling bzzzzzzz. This buzz sounds like it's trying to run somewhere, and now like it's pushing someone over in the playground, it's angry. I can't see it. It must be a fly. Somewhere. I climb on to my bed and bounce, eyes jumping here and there over the ceiling. There in the corner, above the door, is a wisp of a spider's web, but no one is home, and there are no prisoners. I bounce higher, the eiderdown squidges up under my toes; Sweetieflower thumps to the floor. The buzzing stops for a second. *Oh poor Sweetieflower*, I say, jumping down. I sit and hug my naked dolly; the buzzing starts again but this time I feel it, the bzzzzzzz is tickling my chest. I hold Sweetieflower out in front of me. Sunlight spikes out her gold sticky-out hair; her eyelashes have grown spindly-long in the light, fairy fingers on chubby cheeks. I shake my doll until her brown eyes open. I don't like them closed, for her to be dead like Granny Davy.

Bzzzzzzzz. Bzzz. BZZZZZZZZZZ. It's inside her. Something is flying inside her head. I think that I would hate a fly zooming around my thoughts. I hold her on my lap and pull at her head. It doesn't take much. She has a weak neck; Daddy is always carrying Sweetieflower off to the Dolls' Hospital to have her head reattached. In the second that her golden head parts from the body, a whirr of black and yellow flies into my cheek. I feel the soft burr of its wings push away from my face. I let out a scream, I don't want it in my hair; it's a giant beast, not a fly. How did it fit into her head?

I crouch behind my bed, holding on to her body. Bzzzz bzzzzzzz the thing rushes round my room, it swoops up to the ceiling then drops down to my books, then it flies up again, and bashes straight into the window.

'What on earth happened?' My mother appears at the door; her eyes find the beast immediately. 'Did it sting you? No. Lucky girl. A wasp, at this time of the year! … It must've fallen asleep.' My mother opens the window and shoos it out. Then she picks up Sweetieflower's head that has rolled into the middle of the room.

'Let's get her back in one piece. And how about some clothes, she must be chilly.' But I'm stuck still, wondering how it can be that the wasp can make a bed in my doll's head, and why Granny Davy couldn't be put back together in one piece.

Afterwards, I'm lonely. Sweetieflower sits all by herself on top of my bookshelves. She's still my best doll, but we don't play anymore. Daddy says it's raw gooseberries that give me the collywobbles but it isn't, my tummy hops around scary things, like when ghosts play hide-and-seek, or when I think about leaving – like Granny Davy – or when I pick up Sweetieflower and hear the buzzing again. I can't touch her but I hope she's not crying inside.

When Emily was born, we were living in Somerset and both my parents worked long hours at their restaurant in Ilminster. We had a Norland Nanny, Jane, to help look after us; she was nineteen and newly qualified. Her surname, Tottle, used to make me laugh because her firm step was nothing like a totter or a toddle. Jane made everything fun: we danced between crocuses, built space ships with egg boxes, went for adventures in her maroon Mini, her white gloves gripping the steering wheel as she sang with me.

My parents would try and persuade Jane not to wear her uniform but she said she was proud to wear it. And there was something comforting about the fawn dress with its starched white collar and the soft brown cardi, and the nurse's watch on her chest, and more fundamentally, about her clothes not changing. When we went out, she looked like Mary Poppins; a brimmed hat angled on her carefully pinned bun, and a matching taupe coat that nearly reached her ankles.

Jane became part of the family, so much so that after our parent's marriage dissolved she remained in touch, sharing her wedding plans and writing letters to me in her distinctive rounded handwriting that I found easy to read. When Emily and I were about seven and three, she came to visit us at Nom's during the Easter holiday with her husband Geoff, whose slicked black hair made him look like a film star from the black-and-white films my father had been showing me. Nom had told us to be gentle, because Jane had been 'a little bit poorly'. But she was unrecognisable. Her eyes, nose and mouth were barely visible, her face was crowded with oozing red- and yellow-crusted open sores; her long hair had almost all gone and she was so thin that she looked as if she might snap in half. She sat in Granny Davy's tall chair, her lap conspicuously empty. Normally I would have leapt up, but I couldn't look at her. She wasn't Jane, and Emily and I jumped all over Geoff instead.

A couple of weeks later, when we were back in Hampstead, Geoff wrote to say that cancer had been too much for his beautiful, young wife; Jane had died. As Mummy read out the letter my stomach felt hollow, even though I had just swallowed sadness bigger than anything I could have imagined. Whenever I heard the word *cancer* thereafter, I would see Jane's open face and her smile that had twinkled me out of any sulk, and then Jane disfigured by the disease that stole her away. Her empty lap haunts me still.

GARGOYLES

'Mummy, Daddy, Emily, Grandma, Nom, Munroe (dog), Leo (cat), Enid, Robert, Timothy, Janice, Richard, Amanda, Jonesey, Peter ... please God, keep them alive and well, let nothing bad happen to them.' I'd think this prayer as I huddled down in my bed at Rookesbury, before sleep took me. If I woke in the small hours, freezing cold, with the thought that I'd left someone out, or put them in the wrong order, I'd apologise to God and pray again, making sure that I included everyone. If I didn't, something appalling would surely befall one of the listed. Poor them, it wasn't their fault that I'd included them in this list. My religious education more or less stuttered to a halt when I left Rookesbury at twelve, but I continued to pray, with gilded superstition. Even when it didn't work:

Steph is the new babysitter. She's sitting in the armchair by the telephone, her blond hair scrunched back into a huge ponytail, her cheeks are highlighted with stripes of yellow blusher that meet wings of pink eyeshadow. But it's her mascara that fascinates me the most; both eyes are fringed with heavy-legged centipedes. Emily's watching television.

'Are you going to draw their bodies?' I ask.

'Uh ... no,' Steph says, detailing pointy faces on a spiral notepad, strands of her backcombed fringe falling into the biro etchings. *You'll like Steph, she's doing A-Level Art*, my mother had said when I protested at having a babysitter at the age of thirteen.

The phone rings. Steph answers. 'Yuh ... Oh no... Is she all right? ... No, my dad's collecting me at ten. Yuh, okay. I'll see if I can. Yuh, I'll tell them. Okay. Bye.' She hangs up.

'That was your mum's boyfriend.'

'Peter?' I say, trying to ignore how nervousness has shouted

107

down indifference in her voice. Emily has come to sit by me.

'Yuh. It's your mum. She's uh had a car accident. She's being X-rayed at the hospital now.' Steph picks up the phone again.

'Is my mum okay?' She's dialling.

'He said she's having her neck X-rayed. Wait … Hello? Dad? Yuh it's me. Their mum's had a crash; she's at the hospital. They want me to stay the night … no … okay, well can you come later then, to pick me up? I'm sorry, Dad … It's not my fault … Okay. Bye, Dad.' Her dad's angry voice had been leaping out of the receiver.

'Do you think my mum really is okay?' My heart is missing beats, and my fingers are icy. I hear the screech of tyres, the smash of car on car, and see a windscreen in smithereens, splinters of glass made redder and more precious than rubies by my mother's blood. I see nothingness circling.

'Yuh. Look, don't worry. Don't you think you should go to bed now?' Steph goes back to her pointy faces. Emily and I sit close together, watching the TV screen; we jump at the sound of every car stopping outside the house. I squeeze her hand. The phone rings again. It's the first time I've ever wanted it to be Peter ringing.

'Hello, yuh … No my dad says I can't stay the night. He's picking me up at midnight, whatever. Oh. Okay. Yuh. I'll tell them. Okay. Bye.'

'What did he say?' I ask.

'He says that they're gonna let your mum out soon and then they'll come back.' A whoosh of lightness hits my head, my heart calms.

'Shall I make you some tea, Steph?' I ask with outsized brightness.

'Uh … yuh. Okay. Two sugars.'

'Can we make Mummy one too?' says Emily, reaching on tiptoes to get milk out of the fridge.

'It's probably just what she'll need.' I get down a couple more mugs.

When the keys rattle in the lock, we rush to the door. As it opens, Peter pulls out the keys. My mother is behind him; she's yellowy white against the inky night.

'I'm fine.' Her smile wobbles above a foam collar. 'It's just a bit of whiplash,' she says as Peter helps her over the flood step that separates our house from the pavement.

'About time. C'mon Steph, get your cash.' Steph's dad, a small, balding man, had arrived a few minutes earlier. He pushes past Peter and my mum and disappears out of the front door.

Thank you for letting my mum be okay, I say when I eventually get to bed, before reciting my list of names to be safe. I had been trying to forget about the list; *if anyone got into your head and heard it, they'd think you so childish*, I rebuke myself. But if I hadn't said it last night, who knows.

Our GCSE Biology teacher, Mrs Corney, was kindly faced with pink veins crisscrossing her cheeks; she leaned back against the edge of the whiteboard, her grey curls flattened into the medusa-mass of red and blue arrows demonstrating the heart's blood flow. We'd strayed from ventricular specifics to heart attacks and then to dying. The big full stop.

'I think … I think too much about dying,' I had said. Her rheumy blue eyes were deep in thought.

'What part of death worries you, Harriet?'

'Um … you know, the process, the moment of dying … The nothingness afterwards. What happens in nothingness … it happening suddenly … to my family, to me … and friends.'

'Actually, it's very difficult to die,' said Mrs Corney. 'The body has so many intricate lines of defence, it takes an awful lot to get past them.' Her words were an arm round my shoulder that I cozied into; she was a nurse for twenty years, so she should know, I reminded myself, when I fought against the whirlpool lip threatening to curl over me, and swallow me down into forever swirling thoughts of nothingness.

'If I become ill, or start losing my marbles, I'll get in a boat and sail off ... and that'll be that.' My father took another swig of cider. Lunchtimes with my father and Nom were intense. Ever since I could remember, the fat, faded navy dictionary would be on hand for Emily and me to use when there was a word we didn't understand. There was never any chitchat; he was particularly scornful of his sister, who made a habit of mentioning the weather. At nine years old, I'd listen to his discourses on nature and nurture and conditioning; it was around then that I made the connection between cider and the colour of his language.

'But what would you eat? Who would look after you?' I asked, my head suddenly full of him starving, clinging to the rigging of a small boat being tossed high by monster waves.

'Harriet, how many times do I have to tell you not to speak with your mouth full?' my father said too quietly.

'Sorry, Daddy. I was just thinking.'

'Well that'd be the whole bloody point, wouldn't it? I wouldn't need food, or anyone. I'd be sailing out to bloody die.'

And this is what my father chose to do some twenty-five years later, in a metaphorical boat:

Emily and I sit on crimson velour upright chairs in front of Mr Pidgeon's desk. In spite of stumbling around the desert of grief for the past few days, ever since my mother broke the news of my father's death, I am trembling with the effort of suppressing laughter and plug my mouth and nose with a tear-sodden handkerchief. *Oh*

Christopher ... Really. Will you stop that awful guffawing! Daddy's laugh exasperated Nom, especially when she was concentrating on her crossword. This would make him guffaw harder. My eyes slide sideways to Emily, she nudges my leg with her knee. Mr Pidgeon the undertaker has produced a glossy brochure to show us the many variety of coffins at our disposal. His sausage fingers are finding the shiny pages a palaver; he raises his right forefinger to his lips and finds his tongue tip, whitened with a crest of saliva; his finger dips into the minute popping bubbles and he's able to turn the brochure's pages with wet alacrity. There's nothing avian about Mr Pidgeon, ha ha ha ... he looks like a butcher ha ha ha, I tell my father.

When the curtains are pulled open almost two hours later, Elsa and Mr Mohammed are fast asleep; the emptiness opposite is blinding. There is no trace of Reg, it's as if he and his long-suffering wife had never been in our midst. Mrs Corney's words are no longer of comfort.

Chapter Eight

A Darkness Descending

Editor's Note: Both myself and the author have taken the decision to censor some details in the following essay for the purpose of obscuring identities.

I was much teased at Sixth Form College for my obsession with *Tess of the D'Urbervilles*. Partly responsible for my preoccupation with the A-Level text was our teacher. Don McGovern looked as if he had stepped out of a Renaissance painting and his deep, resonant voice always seemed in resistance to his pallor. He conducted our classes as if they were university seminars; he might as well have been taking us on potholing expeditions, shining his torch on diamond-dripping stalactites, such was his illumination of Chaucer's *Canterbury Tales*, and Hardy's prose. Essays were handed back annotated in his elegant forward-sloping script, exhibiting the same meticulous attention to detail that he inspired in close reading of texts. It was Don's understated passion for literature and his own conscientiousness that made me want to not only do well, but to excel – an optimistic desire, considering I had just spent a year retaking my GCSEs.

Unsurprisingly, one of our course essays was entitled, 'Tess, a pure woman. Discuss.' Since its publication in 1891, *Tess of the D'Urbervilles – A Pure Woman*, has sparked controversy.

And considering the austere moral climes of Victorian England, a society light years from the #MeToo movement, it's of little wonder Hardy had difficulties in securing a publisher following the novel's serialisation in *The Graphic* newspaper. His unmarried heroine, Tess Durbeyfield, gives birth at eighteen, the baby's conception lying at the crux of the novel's debate. Was Tess raped or seduced by Alec D'Urberville? The infant is sickly and dies. Tess marries Angel Clare a couple of years later. Her efforts to confess her past beforehand are thwarted, and on discovery, he leaves her, temporarily. She subsequently stabs D'Urberville to death. On writing the essay, I acknowledged that there is no explicit language of assault with regard to her loss of virginity; the violation is implicit. Why? Hardy, of course, would have been conscious of his audience's sensibilities, and his use of ambiguity suggested it was more of a Trojan horse, in that it might provoke a wider discussion about rape and the depiction of women than had the assault been detailed. There was no doubt in my mind that Hardy's portrayal of Tess screamed her innocence and vulnerability. I focused, somewhat predictably, on his choice of subtitle, and epigraph:

'... Poor wounded name! My bosom as a bed
Shall lodge thee.'
– Shakespeare, *Two Gentlemen of Verona*

and cordoned off The Chase and other places of interest, scouring the text, forensically collating the portentous events, and changes of landscape (for Tess's character is intrinsically associated with her surrounding environment) preceding the 'encounter' in England's oldest woodland, on that foggy night. I sought to show the rape was unquestionable; that the violation could not taint her innate purity, in spite of the aftermath. Even before writing the essay I had felt a curious affinity with Tess as I shadowed her through the immense Vale of Blakemore – *for the most part untrodden* – and Wessex; unconsciously wiping droplets of warm blood from my skin, following the deaths of Prince – the Durbeyfields' horse – and later, D'Urberville. My passion was weird, and my peers thought so too, giggling and calling out 'Tessy!' as I passed them on the way to other lessons, even those who were not doing English A-Level. Here is not the place to submit my final list of evidence. Don was, however, convinced, and awarded me his first A (no A* back in those days).

Anna Karenina, fellow towering tragic heroine, also much moved me, yet she didn't settle down in my thoughts with the same weight as Tess. I never wondered at the time about my curious affinity, nor asked myself why I let this particular protagonist occupy so much headspace. I'd thought quite a lot about rape as a schoolgirl. Indeed, apart from worrying that the Thames was about to burst its banks, there being only a road and a wall separating it from our terraced house, and the flood barrier yet to be completed – and that Reagan, Thatcher and the Kremlin were, at any given moment, minutes away from unleashing a world-popping missile – what scared my thirteen-year-old self the most on her way home from school, satchel slung over shoulder, was being raped. At the time, newspaper headlines collocated the upcoming royal nuptials of Charles and Diana with the arrest and subsequent trial of the Yorkshire Ripper. I wasn't a fan of scary films or books, so it's unclear what drove my compulsion to read article after article detailing the atrocities and their timelines, the lives of the thirteen women he'd killed, and the apparent failures of the police investigation. In so doing, I pasted the grainy black-and-white image of a smirking Sutcliffe that fronted broadsheets and tabloids alike to the back wall of my mind. I'd stare at his photograph and become lost down the tunnel of his T-trimmed beard, wondering about the terrified women. And it was this photo of Sutcliffe that would jump out at me if journeying home from school late, and alone.

I assumed all rapists raped like Sutcliffe, deducing from his trade-tools – the knives, hammers and screwdrivers – that if you were raped you would most likely die. When I thought about it happening, it was always the prelude –

– I'd watch a girl get off the train at Barnes station, the creepiest location nearest to where I lived, and she'd be on the deserted platform tracking the window that framed the flames of orange and red seats until the carriage disappeared into the night. It's cold. Hands clenched deep into her duffle coat pockets. She goes down the steps. Past cars parked at the station entrance. The road is more lane and woodland than city, and the trees are ancient, wide enough for a platoon to secret themselves. She's limping, not walking at her usual speed; uneven pavement catches the hole in her right sole. Her footsteps echo. A street light flickers, and the moon's on the wane. Bushes rustle, and a vixen screeches, somewhere close. It's drizzling; she smells the fox and wet leaves, and the road's all glittery. Footsteps. A glance over her shoulder, and no one's there. Brisker, firmer steps, and she turns to look, heart racing, and out of the darkness he's there. Her screams muted by nicotine-stinking fingers that slam her mouth, top lip mashed into teeth. She's dragged through thorny bushes. Pushed down. Wet undergrowth. Shoe comes off. He's above her. Breathing heavily. Bearing down. Balaclava. Sour body stench. He removes his hand, he's got her scarf, he's going to gag her. Heart beating so fast she hears the blood in her ears. She scratches at his covered face; tries to push him off and there's a whip of blade. Its pressure icy on her neck.

The whole scene was then yellowed ... My brain balked whenever I crept towards the verb, pixelating clumsy images with yellow and the fields of rapeseed flower that had bordered my junior school, as if it were a personal alarm. At that age I had no experience of sex other than biology classes and a book given to me on The Facts of Life ('Remember, vagina rhymes with South Carolina'). Sex was abstract, something that happened to adults and occasionally to characters in the books I read.

Hormones eventually kicked in, and on holiday in France a muscular lifeguard had instructed me *'ouvert ta bouche'* behind the sun loungers, and I had my first kiss. At fifteen, I was spending my Martin's newsagent Saturday job wages on blue and silver eyeshadow and pots of gloopy hair gel to spike my hair. My grey school uniform skirt was rolled up, and my toes were scrunched in pointy shoes in the vain attempt to fit in with my classmates. I was the moodiest teen alive, habitually snapping at my family; hating myself for it, even as venom spewed from my lips. Among all the teenage angst resided the same old fear, and when the school magazine chose Horror as its theme that year, they published my poem about a rainy, dark walk home, that closed with the assailant's ghostly face.

It was, then, a combination of immaturity and naivety that sketched my Sutcliffesque identikit of the stranger rapist. For when it did happen, the inconceivable-conceivable, it could not have been further from Barnes station and the balaclava-clad perpetrator. Less than a year after I'd written the poem, ███ ████████████████████████████████████ –

– Up the cliff path, it's a steep climb, and the wind nips round my ankles, mocking my Ken High Street Market cropped jeans. He's just a few steps ahead, *Come on*, he says, *it's not far*. He wants to show me the view. An elderly couple in matching anoraks smile as they approach us on their way down, her eyes blue-green as the sea glinting below. *Good afternoon*, he says, grinning and stopping still to ease their way past, and I wonder whether they think he's my father. I was sixteen two weeks ago; he's ████

██

██

██

██

██

████████████████████████████████. *Come on, Slow Coach*, he
urges now, grabbing my hand; *we need to fitten you up*, he says
with a meaningful look. I think of my father, grandmother and
Emily and our Cornish cliff walks. I picture my mother at work,
believing me to be having a marvellous time. *Right, here we are*,
he says. We've veered off the main path, gorse bushes, purple
flowers. *Here we are*, he repeats and pulls me towards him. He
kisses me, his tongue's cold, and I smell honey and almond. And
washing powder. I pull away. *What's this?* he says, kneeling and
simultaneously yanking me towards him, down to the ground. I
try to get up. *There's a word for someone like you*, he says, his tone
suddenly fierce. *You're a little pricktease … You wanted this.* He's
unzipping his khaki trousers and undoing the buttons of mine.
No! I say, squirming. *This is an exciting day, losing your virginity's
an exciting day*, he says. My whole body cringes, and then I'm
flooded with absolute relief: he can't do anything: *I have my
period*, I say, assuming this will put an end to it all. He's got my
trousers down. *Really?* He stops tugging, looking me in the eye,
and his washing powder scent tells me it'll be okay. *Take it out*, he
says. *What?* I say, not understanding. *You can still have sex, even if
it's the time of the month … so, take it out*, he repeats. *Whatever it is
you've got up there.* Something about his voice and his narrowing
eyes makes me obey. My cheeks burn, appalled, as he watches
me. He rummages in his jacket pocket, his jacket that he's still

wearing in spite of his exposed, protruding Y-fronts, and he pulls out a tissue and lays it on the ground, beside me. *Put it there*, he says, as if talking to a child. *You can pop it back up after.*

I remember this preamble vividly, even the brownish blood on the ridged tampon as if it were some gratuitous modern art exhibit. Of the actual act, I remember the ground, scratchy under my skin; it taking him several stubby attempts; I clearly hear my voice saying, *No!*; that he called me a *pricktease*, again; his grunts; seagulls squawking. When he was inside, it hurt, even in my head. What I can't remember, though, is his face at that point. Clarity returns afterwards. When he stands above me, all smiles, zipping up his trousers, having a look over his shoulders. *We were lucky,* he says conspiratorially, *that no one disturbed us ... You put it back in yet? ... Right, up you get. Why the long face?* When I stand up, shaky, he walks me a couple of metres towards the cliff edge. Hands squarely on my shoulders. *Right, shout it to the world,* he says. I'm feeling sick. I'm not sure what he wants me to shout. *Go on, then,* he says with a little push. The cliff-top edge is too close, and I step back. *What must I say?* I ask. *Not say, I want you to shout, Hurray! I'm not a virgin anymore!* His voice has lost its fatherly singsong tone. I can't. The words won't come. *Go on,* he says, grip firmer on my shoulders. I focus on the horizon. *Hurray. I'm not a virgin anymore.* It wasn't a shout. I hear my voice, flat, and my words plummet.

That ███████ wasn't a stranger, or resembled Sutcliffe in any way; that he didn't threaten with a knife or hammer; that it happened in broad daylight; that I didn't scratch or punch him off me; that I didn't run away; that he smelt of moisturising lotion and Persil; ████████████████████████████; ███████ ███████████; that he had kissed me a few months before, when I was fifteen, and I hadn't done anything about it (*it's our little secret,* he said, *no one will believe you anyway*); that I'd worn a denim miniskirt in his presence; that I didn't tell ████████, or my mother, for fear of hurting them, or report it to the police … all these facts conspired to confuse, and bury the most important fact of all, my resolute *No*, for years. It was not a physically brutal rape; there were no visible cuts or bruises (just cystitis). His actions, however, were calculated: he had waited until I was just sixteen. Coincidence or not, I failed all my GCSEs that summer; and for the next two or three years I wandered around with eyes that had been forced open before they were ready; and although my behaviour was not promiscuous, I certainly became sexually precocious in that period, and had encounters that were numbing. That I always regretted.

It was around the time I reread *Tess* in my mid-twenties, having found myself a red-cloth, sumptuously threadbare 1927 edition at a Hay-on-Wye bookshop, that the penny began to drop. I realised that Don McGovern's superlative teaching had not only brought Tess Durbeyfield's beating heart close to me, it had also shone its torch to expose ███████ as the rapist he was, and will forever be.

Tess tells her brother, Abraham, that they live upon a *blighted* star.[42] This is near the beginning of the novel, when they're on their way to hoick out their drunken father from Rolliver's Inn. It's the middle of the night, and they're travelling by horse and cart with Tess at the reins. They fall asleep. There's a ghastly collision in which we see Prince, their father's horse, speared to death by the shaft of a speeding mail-cart. The Durbeyfields can ill afford to replace the horse and Tess feels responsible. In an effort to repay her parents, she obliges their desire to seek work and *claim kin* with a *rich lady out by Tantridge, on the edge o' The Chase*

---

42   Thomas Hardy, *Tess of the D'Urbervilles*, (London: Macmillan And Co, 1927), p.34

of the name of D'Urberville.[43] The lady is an invalid, and Tess's dealings are with her son, Alec D'Urberville. He gives her the job of caring for his mother's chickens. Fast forward a few months, past several of the aforementioned portentous events used as evidence in my A-Level essay, and D'Urberville, on horseback, rescues Tess from a roadside rabble one evening, and takes her home to Tantridge via The Chase, *the oldest wood in England.*[44] She becomes suspicious of his chosen route and demands he sets her down. He does so on the condition that she stays with the horse while he goes to *ascertain*[45] their position as it has become foggy, *which so disguises everything,*[46] and they are lost. She waits, among the trees, and falls asleep upon the leaves where he left her. By the time D'Urberville recognises their whereabouts and finally returns, the moon had gone down and *The Chase was wrapped in thick darkness,*[47] it isn't until he hears the movement of his horse that he locates Tess. Hardy writes:

> The obscurity was so great that he could see absolutely nothing but a pale nebulousness at his feet ... everything else vast blackness alike ... darkness and silence ruled everywhere around ... above them rose the primeval yews and oaks of The Chase ... why was it on this beautiful feminine tissue, sensitive as gossamer, and practically blank as snow as yet, there should have been traced such a coarse pattern it was doomed to receive ...[48]

---

43   Hardy, *Tess of the D'Urbervilles*, p.33

44   Hardy, *Tess of the D'Urbervilles*, p.87

45   Hardy, *Tess of the D'Urbervilles*, p.88

46   Hardy, *Tess of the D'Urbervilles*, p.88

47   Hardy, *Tess of the D'Urbervilles*, p.90

48   Hardy, *Tess of the D'Urbervilles*, pp.90–1

Tess's loss of virginity and assault is invisible against the leaves where she lay, and shrouded in foggy darkness. Back in my A-Level classroom, the East Sussex cliff walk must have been too close for me to realise that the affinity I felt was anything more than a deep appreciation for Tess's strength of character, or to note that D'Urberville didn't fit my Sutcliffesque rapist's profile. But somewhere in my subconscious the torch must have been far-reaching, to eventually penetrate the fog.

My rage has increased over the years; unlike Tess, I've never wanted to kill ████████ but I've dwelt on how he might be made to suffer, and be humiliated. ████████████████ ██ ██████████████████████████. And when I think about someone molesting or raping either of my nieces, I am wracked with nausea and boiling rage. I think then I would be in danger of committing murder. I feel a similar churning sickness whenever I read of rapes in the news. And I'd set Tess loose on the despicable uncle in Eimear McBride's A Girl is a Half Formed Thing and on Yeong Hye's husband, Mr Cheong, in Han Kang's The Vegetarian. Some questions won't go away, however many times I answer them. As someone who often takes too literally the words people choose to use in conversation, it's worried me that he called me a pricktease; how could he have thought me a temptress? And what was he doing, a man nearly ████, wanting sex from a fifteen/ sixteen-year-old? Much darkness transpired in the bright seaside light on that day.

Chapter Nine

'When's your baby due, dear?' Mrs Mohammed asks, putting down her book and rising from the chair next to my bed. Her voice is smoky cashmere, but each syllable snags on her jingling bangles as she points to the steep gradient of my stomach. This is the first time she has initiated conversation; usually her eyes dart an unspoken question, *Shall I sit with you for a while?* Whatever answer she finds in my face allows her to sink into the blue chair and read for twenty minutes or so before returning to Mr Mohammed. But the only word she actually murmurs – until now – is *Hello*, barely moving her lips; this ordinary little word of greeting colours her expression as any vibrant shade of lipstick. I shake my head and smile, *No baby.* I scramble around for the words to explain that my tummy is distended with blood and lump, but my mind is pitch black.

'Oh dear, I hope I haven't upset you,' she says, her hand sidesteps the cannula and clasps my fingers, and they thaw in its warmth. I shake my head again; *No, of course not.* I thought the smile had sufficed, yet my eyes have betrayed me, and she's spotted the root nerve poking up through the camouflage, crushed beneath her velvet tread. I am livid with myself for embarrassing Mrs Mohammed.

When Emily and I were teenagers, it was me that had had the babysitting jobs.

Oh Harriet has such a way with children, adults would bray. Harriet as mother was a foregone conclusion amongst those knowing observers, and for me too. But their tealeaves conjured me in floral frocks and Volvos, whereas *my babies*, with their made-for-laughing-big-cheeks, cooed and gurgled from the back and bounce of an ancient Land Rover that jalopied across my mind, over hill and valley to Farmer Llewelyn and his ailing heifer; *I will become a vet first.* Whatever the route, motherhood was as engrained on my path as the gold-leaf on Nom's wooden Madonna icon hanging above her bed. In Critical Care, the supermodel nurse that helped harness my runaway heart had returned to my bedside with a frown gouging her Ethiopian features; *Harriet, please can you confirm your age for me, there's been a mistake, we've had you down as forty all this while* ... She'd emphasised *forty* with a dramatic roll of her eyes. And it is true. In spite of her disbelief, I am six weeks past forty.

Along with my passion for animals, Gerald Durrell and James Herriot were responsible for stoking my veterinary dreams. I wolfed down all their books at Rookesbury. But the fantasy met a logical end when it became apparent that there was more to chemistry and physics than the elegant writing up of experiments, and the sketching of conical flasks – and Bunsen burners – in the manner of Matisse, and that I had as much aptitude for science and maths as I had had for ballet. No one had wanted to Polka-partner the girl who possessed all the coordination of Laurel and Hardy moving a piano from a room filled with priceless ornaments.

And now the dream of having my own family – that has beamed and beckoned like a beacon since childhood – is fading fast; a flicker, faint and anodyne.

Reminders, though, flare. Everywhere:

Angels, shepherds, lambs, the three kings, Mary and Joseph sway and fidget round a doll swaddled in tea towels, propped up in a shopping basket. They are singing 'Away in a Manger'. I'm with Emily and my mother watching Hatch Ride Primary School's nativity play. Alice is already one of the taller children and is standing at the back. Her white angel costume sucks at the colour from her milk-pale face, leaving only the faintest blush on each cheek as she spots me giving her a secret wave. *Pleeease don't do anything embarrassing, Hat,* she'd implored last night on the phone, shortening the name of Hattyroona that she had given me as a two-year-old. *Like what?* I'd asked all innocent but knowing that it took a mere glance to embarrass my nearly seven-year-old niece. *Oh I don't know, like your monkey impression,* she had giggled. *No, I really do mean it Hat,* and her little voice had turned serious. She stands there now, managing to sing and chew her bottom lip at the same time; her Pre-Raphaelite red hair too shiny for the halo that hovers cutely askew.

The stars in the bright sky looked down where He lay ...

I smile. At nursery school, we had lengthened the second *the* and sang it *the-uh*. Tongue dipping into the gap left by a missing front tooth. On the church hall table were loo roll tubes dotted with Copydex glue, then rolled in scarlet crepe paper; yellow, pink and orange bells that I cut out, jagged-edged from the blunt, dolphin-nosed scissors, and stuck over the barrel; glitter sprinkled over smudges of the fishy smelling glue, and finally silver tinsel securing each end of the cracker – a trove of Dolly Mixture sweets rattling from within. We'd made crackers, Chinese lanterns and paper-chain decorations all that day. Before our nativity in the evening.

The cattle are lowing, the baby awakes,

The—uh.

In front of us is a woman with thick tawny hair pulled back in a ponytail, loose curls spiral about the nape of her neck casting intricate shadows on her skin, like a henna tattoo. She sits with a blanket covering the seats of the two adjacent chairs. On the blanket sleeps her baby. Next to me Emily is whispering something about one of the girls to our mother, who stifles a laugh and nods.

Two years younger than her sister, Maddy May is a shepherd clutching a cuddly lamb. She sings each word with careful deliberation, her shining lake eyes enlarging further with every circle of her mouth, as confident as her mother had been at the same age. Emily had not been deterred by the glare of stage lights when she grinned her special smile and pas-de-deuxed across the stage of The Golden Theatre, holding out the netted layers of her skirt straight onto the stage of Old Compton Street's Prince Edward Theatre and into *Evita* with Elaine Paige.

The baby in front whimpers and his mother turns sideways to pick him up; a hand under each of his armpits, the chunky sky-blue cable knit of his cardi squishes up beneath her thumbs. His eyes are now level with hers. He can only be a few weeks old – if that – his face still has that slightly crumpled look and his cheeks are downy. She holds him a fraction closer, making it easier for him to focus. The bruise of tiredness beneath her eyes has disappeared, her face is ablaze with smile and amazed love, she's talking to him but 'O Come all Ye Faithful' is in full chorus and I can't hear what she says ... Her son stares back unblinking, trying to mimic the shape of her smile with his own tiny goldfish mouth. Then she turns back to the nativity with him on her shoulder, I can see that she's rubbing his back and that his eyes are drunk from its rhythm.

And I sit back, and watch my glorious nieces and wonder at all the bad decisions I've made.

And I lie here, my hands resting each side of my distended tummy, with Mrs Mohammed engrossed in soft conversation with Mr Mohammed, and drift in and out of those same mistakes.

*

It's the afternoon. Elsa is chatting to Bert, and Mr Mohammed has his son and daughter-in-law visiting, and my mother is reading me crossword clues.

I am basking in nausea-free bliss.

It is the first time in nearly two weeks that my body is not in spasm from the continual retching.

I visualise a painting, in oils, the canvas is divided simply into two: two-thirds emerald and one-third lapis. I step barefoot into the green; it's deep grass, luxuriant from months of spring rain. I take off the rest of my clothes and lie down. Long blades tickle my shoulders and when I move baubles of dew spill onto my skin; I stretch out and feel, really feel, the early summer rays warm every pore of my skin; I look to the sky, solid blue, not a cloud ...

'Come on, thirteen down ... *natural, inborn* ... in six. It's blank, blank, N, blank, blank, blank. Any guesses?' My mother gently prods my leg.

'Um ... again, please?' My brain's word processor has slowed right down. As I drag myself away from the saturated shades of green and blue, Dr Flower suddenly appears. She has a clipboard.

'So sorry to disturb you,' she says, closing the cubicle curtains. 'Harriet, how are you doing with the Fentanyl patch ... any problems?'

'No, it's okay,' I say, knowing that the question doesn't warrant the clipboard, that they've already asked me this on ward rounds – and finally remembering the name of the actress of whom she reminds me.

'Ah that's good,' she says smiling at both of us. *It's definitely the smile. Gwyneth Paltrow.* 'Well, what we'd like to do a little later today is to give you a blood plasma transfusion.'

'Why?' The blue-green calm has gone. All at once I feel defensive and on edge.

'What will it help with, Dr Flower?' asks my mother from over the top of her reading glasses.

'Well, we think your blood needs a hand with all the clotting it has to do at the moment,' she says, looking at me. 'It's quite painless. And it'll only take half an hour.'

'What are its side effects?' I know already.

'Yes, I should probably run through those with you. It's unlikely but it is possible that you'll experience some reaction. We would be monitoring you extremely closely,' says the doctor, hugging the clipboard to her chest.

'Nausea?'

She nods. 'There's a bit of a list, actually ... fever, facial flushing, vomiting, tight chest ...' She went on but I'd stopped concentrating after nausea had been confirmed.

'No,' I say.

'The clotting is important, Harriet. You don't actually have much of a choice about this. But we do need your consent.' Dr Flower's voice has lost its lightness. I shake my head, aware that my reasoning is suspect.

'The chances are, that you won't be affected by any of the

symptoms I mentioned,' says Dr Flower, 'and it will, of course, aid your recovery.' Her smile has made a swift return. But I don't feel its reassurance. My physical incapacitation is surreal as in nightmare, yet I am cloaking treatment with threat – and sounding nonsensical in the process. I'm fearful that something about Reg's death is contagious, and I'm running from Nausea as if it were the assassin itself.

'Harriet … I think you need to weigh up the benefits against its risks.' My mother's words are measured but the worry that leaps from her eyes reminds me that I shouldn't be thinking of myself. The clipboard is put to use.

At 10 p.m., just as Mr Mohammed and Elsa are readying themselves for sleep, a Dr Singh and John, the nurse that rectified my deflated bed, arrive at my bedside with a trolley on which is an ice-box, tubing and a file of papers that they flick through.

'Right Harriet, we just need to check a few things, and then we can hook you up to the plasma … I just need to make sure you don't have any rash.' Dr Singh examines my skin while John does my obs.

'No fever?' asks the doctor.

'No, I think we're about ready. Okay, Harriet?' John flashes a rare smile. I nod, feeling anything but okay. He removes a bag from the box and inspects it closely; it's filled with a suspiciously straw-yellow looking substance. The bag is connected to the tubing and hung from the IV stand that has been off-duty since the pain relief pump was replaced with Fentanyl patches.

'Can you state your full name and date of birth for me?' Dr Singh is looking at my Patient ID wristband. I tell him and John flushes the dormant cannula on my right arm with saline.

'All you should feel is a very cold sensation travelling up your arm because the plasma is frozen …' Almost instantaneously I feel the coldness and I close my eyes. The red-brick wall crumbles and the faces emerge, mouths open, one of them has a nest of tongues – each one a viper, writhing towards my hair. *The plasma is doing nothing but good*, I tell myself, as I open my eyes and shut out the gargoyles.

John does my obs again.

'It'll only take half an hour and I'll be back to check on you shortly ... but if you feel peculiar, you know, hot ... or wheezy, call me immediately ... Okay?' He pushes the buzzer into my left hand, glances at his watch, and pulls the curtains open. I hadn't noticed that Dr Singh had already slipped out.

'Alright, Darlin'?' says a sleepy Elsa, turned on her side towards me. 'What does it feel like?'

'Iced mango smoothie going up my arm.' I smile.

'Blimey, I hope they got the right bag, cos it don't half look like the colour of a gypsy's kiss!' she says, looking up at the bag. There's a snort of laughter from Mr Mohammed.

'Elsa! You *are* incorrigible. I'm with Toots, I think it's mango.'

John is back, taking my obs,

'Good, good all fine, Harriet ... any itchiness?'

'No ... the coldness goes all the way up to my chest ...'

'That's quite normal. You're doing great. Just try and relax.'

Thanks to Elsa and Mr Mohammed, that is not difficult. And as soon as I am disconnected from the spent plasma bag, I text my mother to say that all is well. Her first reply tells me that I am brave – which I was clearly not today. Her second reply: P.S I'm sure you've been holding your breath: 13 down was *innate*.

Chapter Ten

Beyond Conception

About four years after the angiomyolipoma, I accidentally dropped my keys through the spokes of Hammersmith Bridge. The structural metalwork broke their fall, and they landed on a sill about a metre out of reach. Not only were they my house and car keys, but the fob was a silver moose I'd acquired in Stockholm, where my then fiancé, Moe, lived before he moved to Singapore. Our relationship was floundering, the wedding on the brink of being postponed, and the key-fall suddenly felt as if it might be acutely symbolic. I hotfooted it to a DIY shop, bought some bamboo, gaffer tape and a magnet (that the sales assistant obligingly tested on a heavier bunch of keys than mine), and fashioned a sturdy fishing pole. Back on the bridge, I forced myself to give friendly explanations to curious fellow pedestrians who had stopped to watch me lower the pole. *Yes, it's exactly like that*, I fake-chuckled in agreement with the guy who was describing in detail a magnetic fishing rod game his toddler enjoyed playing, while really wanting to tell him to get lost. The magnet reached my keys, moose head hanging precariously over the ledge. The bridge creaked its familiar sigh with every passing car and bus, and I held my breath. *Careful! Careful! Easy now …* advised the well-wishers. *Do I look stupid?* I muttered, before realising that I literally did, and that it had been unquestionably careless to drop the keys in the first place. The magnet, though, was strong and the fob was securely attached in the no man's land between the ledge and my hands. I kept the bamboo steady, gradually raising it centimetre by centimetre, and as the keys approached touching distance I relaxed enough to remark that the process actually reminded me more of the kids game Operation, where you use tweezers to remove body parts and a buzzer sounds if the tweezers touch the metal edge of the cavity from which the bone or organ is removed. *Were you any good at it?* asked toddler man. *Not bad*, I said while reaching with my left hand to grab the keys. As my fingertips brushed the moose, the keys fell: they plummeted past their previous resting place, and into the Thames below. I could not believe it. They had been within my grasp.

Getting together with Moe after my illness was a surprise; becoming pregnant aged forty-two was unreal.

'Moe?' There was whooshing on the line and background shrieks when I phoned to tell him; I saw cresting waves, ice cream and beach balls.

'Hey, Sweetheart. Can you hear me?'

'Just about. Sounds like you're on the beach?'

'Close. East Coast Park. With my cousin, he's over from Burma, with his son.'

'Wow! How wonderful.'

'You'd love him, the little one. He's very cute. We're about to go for chilli crab. Wanna join us?'

'Sure thing.'

'Where are you ... hang on, what time is it ... 7 a.m.? Are you even up yet?'

'Cheeky. Actually, I'm sitting on the stairs.'

'Why so?'

'Dunno. Just had to sit down ... Moe, guess what?'

'What, what?'

'I'm pregnant.'

His audible leaping up and down, his joy that rocketed 8,000 miles, down the line into my ear, was overwhelming. It felt as if I was watching the scene play out in a Richard Curtis movie. For a while, after hanging up, I stayed sitting on the stairs – the same ones that challenged the paramedics three years previously – unable to absorb the happiness that fizzed around me. Harvey had pushed his whippety nose into my hands, confused by my snotty, sobbing laughter.

Days passed: jagged concerns surrounded the angio-myolipoma, and my age, but as the morning sickness, *the all-day sickness*, pervaded, *the proof of it*, I allowed excitement to simmer. Matt Winkler – one of the first to know since pregnancy hormones increase blood flow to AMLs – immediately arranged a scan at Charing Cross to check all was stable. *Shall we have a little peek, since we're so close?* Nick Burfitt, the radiologist who performed my life-saving embolisation, asked once he had checked the tumour's dimensions. There were still some weeks to go until the dating scan and I was like a child unable to wait until Christmas Day for my present. I felt the pressure of the cold jellied probe on my abdomen, less than 10cm and light years away from the angiomyolipoma; my eyes locked on the screen and I scoured the deep-sea swirls and contours of my own landscape. *Here*, he said after a while, pointing to a minute white flickering in its own cocoon of black space. I blinked and he'd lifted the probe.

In bed at night, and on waking up, my hands rested on my tummy, protective and warm. Despite an encroaching feeling that it was all too good to be true, I gradually allowed myself to think of the flickering foetus as a baby, *our child*, and signed up for daily emails that charted its development. I felt reassured by seeing several women in advanced stages of pregnancy who were older than me at my first midwife appointment. At ten weeks the waistbands on all my clothes were already uncomfortably tight, and I'd gone up two bra sizes. Moe came over a few days before the dating scan and we viewed the properties we'd shortlisted to rent during the pregnancy. As the angiomyolipoma needed regular monitoring he was going to spend more time in London. And when the baby was born we'd move to his apartment in Singapore. I guess had it not been for the AML, it would've been a month or two down the line before we indulged in looking so far ahead.

You can get dressed now. The sonographer's tone had been impatient, as if she had omitted a prefix of *Come on.* I felt my face flush and let go of Moe's hand. In the waiting room there had been a machine for tokens that you bought to exchange for an image of your baby. *We don't have the correct money for the tokens, would you have any change?* Moe asked as soon as she called us, his words tripping over expectations and excitement. She hadn't even smiled then, just nodded. He squeezed my hand while she had moved the probe back and forth over my belly, his eyes, and my eyes fixed on the monitor. I knew she had been taking too long; that she should have been saying something like, *here you are, see this, here? That's the heartbeat. And this is the head.* Her silence had echoed more than just a shoddy bedside manner. *Is it possible you've made an error with your dates?* she had eventually asked. And all defensive I'd said no, because of the window of time that Moe had been in the country. *We'll give it another two weeks, but right now the measurements don't correspond with that of a twelve-week pregnancy. It might be non-viable.* While Moe pummelled her with questions, I was thinking about the day I had the first scan at Charing Cross. That evening, when I'd got up from the sofa. A sharp pain had fallen from just below my belly button. As if something had snapped. A ping. Glass shattering. I'd mentioned it to the GP. *Any cramps?* she asked. I'd shaken my head, no. *There would've been cramps if it was anything to worry about,* she'd soothed.

It was probably just at the wrong angle, Sweetheart. You'll see, Moe said after the sonographer left the room. He was fuming too about her impersonal, *no, downright rude* manner. In the car I phoned Emily. *I don't understand ... I'm feeling so sick, I have to get up to pee at least three times at night, how can it be?* I keep asking her. *Well there you are, try not to worry,* she says. In her voice I heard her shoving a pillow over the mouth of her own anxiety. Deep down I knew that there was no room for mistake with my dates, and each time I tried a positive thought it was obliterated by the sonic boom of a ping, and that sensation of falling.

It was termed a silent miscarriage. An internal scan a fortnight later confirmed the sonographer's findings. I was booked in for an ERPC (Evacuation of Retained Products of Conception) on a warm day in late June. A month after the procedure I experienced the usual cramping of my period; it lasted several days, but I didn't bleed. *Not to worry, it'll take a while for things to get back to normal,* the GP said. Exactly four weeks later the cramping returned. This time I was certain something was wrong. My uterus felt as though it was ready to erupt; such was the intensity of pain and odd feeling of fullness. Once more, I was advised that all was well, that it was just a matter of time ... *or, could it be,* the GP smiled, *that you're pregnant again?* A further month, and the cramping deep in my lower back and stomach were constant. *Please, listen,* I said to the obstetrician, *my body works like clockwork ... not even a catastrophic haemorrhage interrupts my cycle. Something is wrong.* He scanned me for reassurance purposes and found my womb full of blood; *some material's blocking things, and the blood can't escape.* The evacuation was repeated and my body 'normalised' exactly four weeks later.

It seemed, that summer, as if every woman I passed in the street or park was pregnant.

The force with which the hormones rampaged and occupied my mind was frightening and there was something primeval about the unreachable ache at my very core. I felt out of control, crazed with grief and disbelief. As much as I understood that my age and/or a chromosomal abnormality would have been the likely cause of the miscarriage, I blamed myself: I was the keeper of my body, after all, and it was *me* that had dropped an all-precious being. It was *definitely* the paracetamol I took for a migraine. Why had I agreed to have the extra scans? They had been stressful. It was *clearly* the stress. Why had I continued with long dog walks and swims? And then I was livid for having allowed myself to hope and dream, to imagine the reality of being a mother, after having pretty much come to terms with remaining childless. *How stupid can you be? Of course it was never going to happen.* I didn't know what to do with myself. And I lay on my bed, cradling my empty tummy, crying until there were no more tears. Moe was as supportive as he was able. I was most probably a horror at the time, scornful of all placatory sweetness. I resented that he could walk away from it, *had to be* away on business while I was having the second operation, return to Singapore, work, and enjoy a day of golf. But I was grateful for his honesty, relieved to hear him articulate that which I suspected: *I am sad, but not overwhelmed. Because we can try again.* And he was right in the sense that he could not be overwhelmed by it; as for trying again, his naive optimism infuriated me. Time, of course, did its thing, the hormones settled and I became healthily sad rather than precariously sad.

In her insightful history *Lost*,[49] Shannon Withycombe traces the changing perceptions of miscarriage in nineteenth-century America, weaving together women's writing with hospital

---

[49]   Shannon Withycombe, *Lost: Miscarriage in Nineteenth Century America* (USA: Rutgers University Press, 2018)

records and medical literature of the era. The clinical perspective is fascinating, but what makes Withycombe's book so compelling is the clarity with which the women's voices – and their varying tones of anguish, ambiguity and joy – resonate from the cave of silence long associated with miscarriage. Their moving stories shed light on the disparate reasons why women are reluctant to speak about it still today. It's evident from Withycombe's research that whatever emotions the miscarriage evokes, a sense of social failure bleeds too – from failing to conform to the childbearing norm, and for some women, not being as devastated as those around them believe they should be. From my own experience, I have found it especially perturbing to witness how some mothers perceive childless women. It starts with cheery questions: *How many have you got? How old are yours?* When I reply that I don't have children, the shutters clatter down. Perhaps we're no longer of interest because it's assumed if you haven't had children you're unable to empathise with motherhood, or worse, there must be something intrinsically lacking within you and you're therefore less of a person. Others pity you, and tell you not to worry for *motherhood isn't all it's cut out to be ... it's actually a lot of hard work, you know*. I don't want to embarrass them and bite my lip to stop myself from saying, 'BUT I NEARLY DID. I had a miscarriage. A complicated one,' and then I'm furious for even thinking about justifying myself, or the miscarriage, because the reason for being childless, be it from a life choice or accident of nature, is immaterial.

On more self-indulgent days, the drawn-out process of my miscarriage brings to mind the snail in Frida Kahlo's portrait of her miscarriage in *Henry Ford Hospital* (1932), but I have always been grateful for the medical technology that resolved my physical complications. Reading the women's stories in *Lost* reminded me of this, and also of the psychological benefits of ultrasound scans, particularly for those women who don't feel pregnant until they've seen images of their developing foetus. Withycombe elaborates on the history of foetal visualisation and personification and explores how it can impact a woman's perception of pregnancy and miscarriage. I didn't need a scan to help me feel pregnant, but I was certainly impatient to *see* the evidence of life. There's no doubt that the images in the literature given to me by healthcare professionals, and the website I signed up to, and the flickering presence of that first early scan, all encouraged me to imagine a fully formed future for the nascent being within me. (This was in contrast to the abrupt and imageless *What-To-Expect* ERPC leaflets where the reader was presumed to instantly view her pregnancy as mere *retained product*.)[50] However, the images themselves didn't influence my loss. It was way too primal for that.

No amount of gaffer tape, bamboo and magnet could save our relationship, and several months after the moose hit the river, Moe and I parted ways. (He now has a young family; he was always bound to make a brilliant father.) Despite the comic scene on Hammersmith Bridge, the finality with which the keys had plummeted was reminiscent of the curious pain that fell from my belly button. So quick, and sharp, and with the plangency of a star falling from the sky. Those keys were swaddled with hopes and dreams as they plunged into the Thames. Dreams, born of innate desire and life. And still today, an eight-year-old child will stop me in my tracks, and make me wonder.

---

50   I believe ERPC has been renamed Surgical Management. And I acknowledge, of course, as Withycombe emphasises, there are women who are not unduly disturbed by miscarriage and who would not be offended by such semantics.

Chapter Eleven

Sedate, clipped footsteps: if they were musically transcribed, each cello-deep step would be punctuated with a semibreve, and a tinkle of piccolo (for I hear clinking glass too). From my bed I watch, through the windowed wall, doctors and nurses in discussion at the nurses' station – some faces share a raucous joke, other expressions are intense; during daytime the resounding hubbub muffles footfall from the corridor, making tread distinguishable only in its urgency or heel type (high heels are spikily staccato compared to the stretchy squeak of soft soles). An exception is Faith, which is probably because of the percussion of her crutches. Their clunk and rattle still gooseflesh my thoughts to a standstill. But warm Familiarity – the courtier that treads alongside this approaching low steady rhythm – has also broken the nurses' station sound barrier.

'Susan,' I say to my mother. And a few moments later my boss walks onto the ward. She's dressed in her trademark black, save for the wave of gold De Vroomen brooch on her jacket; her dark hair is immaculately coiffured, curled chin-length, and those sea-tone eyes – that are sweeping the ward – illuminate her face, alabaster-perfect make-up as usual. It's the weighty carrier bag in each hand that drags her regal countenance into incongruity, like a Photoshopped image of the Queen.

'Susan! How kind of you to come. Harriet recognised your footsteps ... what have you got there? ... Here, have my chair.' My mother bustles around our visitor.

'Oh thank you, Elly,' she says, handing over the bags and then coming forward to kiss me on the cheek. 'I brought you some *Ame*, Harriet. I heard you're only drinking fizzy drinks.' *Ame* is the grape-based drink that Susan drinks non-stop in the shop. She sits down and there's a blur of rose-painted nails and sparkle of diamond as she takes off her gloves and rests them on top of her handbag.

'Thank you,' I say, wanting to say much more; overwhelmed that she's lugged the eight bottles all the way here in spite of her bad back.

'It's the very least I can do.' She scrapes her chair forward to make room for the extra seat that my mother has pulled round.

'You don't look nearly as bad as I'd expected you to look, I really thought you'd look a lot worse,' she says, echoing my brother-in-law; her eyes flitting down to my catheter bag and then to my stomach. 'We've been so worried about you ... ever since the message on that Monday morning.' She turns back to my mother. 'I can't believe you had time to think of us.'

'It was Harriet. She didn't want you to think she had forgotten to turn up.'

'You're normally first to arrive, aren't you?' Susan says to me. 'We thought perhaps you'd got the bus instead of walking, and that you'd been caught up in traffic, although Nye said the A316 had been clear for once. After we opened up, I listened to the messages. And there was one from your mother at 5 *o'clock in the morning*, saying that you were very poorly, in hospital.' She looks down briefly at her hands. 'Well, we couldn't believe it ... I told Nye that it was only on the Saturday evening that I'd thought how youthful you'd looked, the way you skipped off down Paved Court.'

I cannot remember any skipping. But I jigsaw together this information and fathom their shock:

It's three miles to Richmond and the shop from home in Teddington, and takes about forty-five minutes if I walk along the road. But if I leave early, my preferred route is to escape the rush-hour traffic at Twickenham and meet the river as it skirts Eel Pie Island. From there I follow the Thames towpath to Dolby Stereo acoustics: above, in the treetops, parakeets shriek a karaoke rendition of their neighbouring blackbird and robins' lilting ensemble; seagulls swoop and whoop; below – bobbing in the river – coots, moorhens and mallards chatter while a heron perfects an arabesque behind a gauze of reeds. Thud of feet: a jogger passes, then another – in matching neon-yellow vests. On my left, winter-toasted leaves bank the wrought-iron railings of Marble Hill Park. And beyond them squirrels dart about the ramparts of a copse, their shiny eyes bulge, ever watchful for dogs. To my right, the river slaps into shore and boats tethered to a pontoon – *Lady Leanna, Free Spirit,* and *Aquarius,* all faded in colour and snuggled in tarpaulin, clank companionably against one another as a sculler rips through the glistening ripples and peaks, his oars creaking with effort. A Yorkshire Terrier wearing a tartan coat scampers towards me; trailing behind is a young woman, her face cast downwards, talking on her phone:

'It's just so amazing …' [Never has a *zed* been flatter, or more lost in deadpan.]

I look up; the trees are sketched inky and vascular against the wan sky.

'I love that outfit …' she says deep into her mobile.

A tiny feather. The whitest, the fluffiest. A cloud caught on a cat-claw twig.

'Oh really, Mummy?' [Hope bites into her voice.]

Boughs of an oak descend into the river, twisting out of grotesquely upturned roots and trunk. They curve and bend, casting dark, hooped reflections. Loch Ness. Log Ness.

'It *is* the best little outfit ...' [Relaxed, half a giggle.]

The dog yaps. I look back; he's well ahead of her now. He's sniffing at some undergrowth. Probably a squirrel. Or rat.

'Did he register that it was you?' [Anxiety strikes at hope.]

She passes me, gravel crunching – grey beanie hat pulled to her brow – oblivious to everything that is not a part of her conversation.

'But ... did he remember?'

A pair of Canadian geese are coming fast into land, /wɔˈaʊ wɔˈaʊ/ their siren screeches as they skid onto the water. Not even this hullabaloo can drown out the plaintive underbelly of her question.

Seconds pass.

And she is gone. I ponder on the outfit that was meant to trigger memories, on the occasion it was originally worn, on *he* ... his identity.

I've dallied long enough, and veer away from the river and powerwalk past the stuttering exhausts; keeping my head pavement-down. I traipse its uneven lines, fallen leaves and litter, the boot-smashed petals – that have bled into the concrete – and spat-out gum. A fellow pedestrian dares to overtake me. I am propelled by some childish compulsion to accelerate, and then buzz with the cheap thrill of leaving him dawdling in my wake. It's particularly gratifying as it's on the very slight incline of Richmond Bridge.

Once I arrive in Paved Court, I wait – as advised – a few yards away from the shop until I see the lofty figure of Nye, the manager, approach. Navy made-to-measure suit, leather satchel slung over his shoulder. Shoes gleaming.

'Morning,' he says with an Olympic sprint of a smile, and shoots a glance up and down the lane before pushing a key from his gaoler's bunch into the top lock; we go in – careful to keep to the edge of the Persian carpet until he has turned off the alarm. Switch on the lights, then upstairs to dump our bags, turn on the CCTV monitor and for me to get changed into smart gear – dark colours are uniform – and brush the river out of my hair. Nye is already back downstairs, ear to handset, listening for messages. He scribbles down an enquiry and then opens the safes. Vaughan Williams is playing on the CD player. And the second CCTV monitor is running, recording our day. An armed robbery several years back, before my time, necessitates these security measures.

'Remind me to go to the Thai supermarket after work,' he says as I pull on a pair of white gloves and enjoy the hit of their freshly laundered scent.

'What are you making, green curry?' I take the busts displaying the diamond pendants from the safe over to the main window, and position them to their best advantage.

'No. Fishcakes. I need to pick up some galangal and stuff for the red curry paste.' He's dressing the smaller, wedding ring window.

'Is it a recipe from your David Thompson book?' I picture the book's decadent pink silk cover.

'Yup. Dead easy.' He describes each stage of the cooking, from the pestle-and-mortaring to the frying, until *the best little outfit* is suffused with the conjured aroma of lemongrass, garlic, chilli, galangal, lime leaves and whiting.

'Stop! My palate's on fire.'

'Sorry ... thought I took out all the chilli seeds.'

'Oh you know what I mean!'

He gives me a cheeky smirk as he locks up the wedding ring window and heads outside with kitchen roll and Windolene. I heft the stacked three boxes of ring pads from out of the safe and place them, as if they are weightless, onto the mahogany and walnut Victorian mourning table in front of the window. *He could sell a cape to Superman,* Susan has told me many a time, each time more earnestly than the last. Nye is the son she never had. But she is more than right, because he can make any subject pulse with life – whether it be Thai fishcakes, the morning light in Windsor Great Park, Spanish lessons, five-a-side football or a diamond ring. He taps on the door to be let back in having wiped away an eruption of fingerprints that were dotting the window.

The boxes contain solitaires, eternity rings, and three-stones: most are diamonds but there are sapphires, rubies, emeralds, aquamarines and topaz too. Space needs to be made for them all. In my first week at the shop, I had to bend my head round the sheer value of the stock, that I could be chatting to Susan and Nye about an episode of *The Sopranos,* while in each of my hands – as casually as you like – would be a pad of rings that amounted to upwards of twelve thousand pounds. It was crazy, I had come from managing a fine patisserie where a handmade *fraisier* – the glossiest of strawberry cakes, speared with chocolate and fluttering with gold leaf – would cost £3.95 and had to be handled as if it were one of the crown jewels. Whilst unravelling these twin absurdities, there was the challenge of dressing the window, of integrating the ring pads with the earrings, bangles and line bracelets in an attractive and cohesive manner that would magpie the eyes of a passer-by. I knew little about jewellery and didn't even wear a watch – so it wasn't as if I could draw on my personal appreciation of gems for guidance. *There are no rules, everyone has their own way of doing it,* Nye said, but he had drawn me a map of how he filled the window nonetheless. Despite his diagram, I still managed to get hopelessly lost negotiating the archipelago of pads and stands. Eventually, it dawned on me to approach the puzzle photographically.

'Pictures must tell a story, Harry. A startling subject is not enough,' Jocelyn says as we walk down the corridor that leads to the Princess Alexandra Hospital's neonatal ward. He's been commissioned to shoot the hospital's brochure, and as his assistant I'm packed like a donkey, carrying his camera bags. I'm twenty-three, and I've been assisting him for six months, and he drills the same point at every shoot whether it's for *Vogue* or The Royal Parks. Photography pounds his veins; although he does *haute* fashion, documentary projects are his passion. After shoots we head back to his flat in Notting Hill. I'll be sitting cross-legged on his living room floor when Henri Cartier Bresson, Jacques Henri Lartigue, Mary Ellen Mark, Gary Winogrand and his old tutor at Newport, David Hurn, all – at varying intervals – land in my lap; he pulls out their books from his floor-to-ceiling shelves, cigarette smoke swirling about the swing of his gesticulating hands as he extols these giants. Competing with Jocelyn's photography library is his collection of vinyl, and his long fingers quickstep across the record player to switch records as seamlessly as a magician. Then he'll grab back a book, flicking through it to pause at images that he considers particularly powerful and deconstructs them to a soundtrack of Richard Thompson, Neil Arthur, Peter Hammill and Aimee Mann. The pack of Marlboro Red on the coffee table is soon scrunched up – next to an ebbing bottle of single malt – and a new one torn open. I sit in bliss, and get drunk on his passion.

A friend introduced us after I graduated from Lampeter. She'd told him about my interest in photography and we met under the red awning of Café Oriel on Sloane Square. I showed him my little black plastic album of snaps, *Lots of people take pretty pictures, but how many of them are special?* I'd said feeling embarrassed. *You have the eye,* he said, and took me on as his assistant.

Right now I'm loading his second camera with colour slide film, trying to be as inconspicuous as possible, and his daddy-longlegs frame is folded as small as it can go; he points the lens of his Nikon F2 at a premature baby in an incubator. Her skin has a yellowish tinge, and a nappy comes up to her armpits; tubes are connected to her nose and a heavily bandaged wrist. The infant's mother slips her hands through two circular openings; one hand supports her neck, the other adjusts a white cap that gapes about her head. The camera shutter whirrs and clicks, the baby's wizened face is not quite the length of her mother's forefinger and she's all elbows and knees as her scrawny sparrow-chick limbs jerk back and forth in bewilderment – or perhaps in protest.

It was only once I had placed the dynasties of gold and platinum diamond eternity rings – the castle-mounts, the claw-sets, the rubovers, the channel-sets, all fortressed in pads of four, three, and one – into the kingdom of the everlasting, that Nye's window map began to make sense. Two years later, the window is a doddle. After returning the empty boxes to the safe I polish the table. This is the table where it all happens, where engagement rings are chosen; a few clients come in having done their homework and know *the 4C's* (colour, clarity, carat weight and cut) and have a clear idea of what they want, but the majority prefer a full tour of all possibilities. Or, couples come in and choose a ring together, and then this table is a stage and their relationship has star billing: we see everything from the great romance to bling-busting divas strutting the boards with scary presence to acquire the carat they *know* they deserve, and then the men who fall asleep at the performance of their own relationship.

'Coffee?' says Nye halfway up the stairs and, as if on cue, the bell rings. It's Susan. I unlock the door.

'Good morning,' I say, 'you're just in time.'

'Good morning,' she says, smiling. 'That sounds nice, I could really do with a coffee this morning.'

My mother has moved her chair again, round to my left side so that she is facing Susan. I sip some *Ame*. And then close my eyes. I listen to them chatting, their voices trickle into one another ... *I can't believe it's Easter next weekend ... No, where does the time go? ... Is it a busy time for the shop? ... Not really, everyone goes away ... you won't be going anywhere? ... No, I think we'll be here for a little while longer ...*

'You dozed off, darling.'

'Sorry. Susan?'

'She had to get back to the shop, but she told me to tell you she'll be back soon.'

*

The plastic rim of the bedpan has buried into my flesh and is drilling away at bone. I'm still catheterised, but my stomach and intestines are conscientious objectors, and set about the dearth of digestible morsels as if they are feasting on the contents of Henry VIII's banquet-full belly. Fifteen minutes since I buzzed. Forty-five minutes since the orderly lowered the back of my bed and said, *Lift your hips, love. That's right, good girl. All set? Okay, buzz when you're done.* It was a mammoth, cramping effort, all for a solitary rabbit dropping that struck the pan as resonantly as a chime from Big Ben, and flushed me with shame. Mr Mohammed would surely have looked up from his tome, and Elsa from her newspaper.

Twenty minutes. I want to buzz again. *Be patient.* But my legs and spine are charging in revolt; I'm hurting. So I go ahead and press the buzzer. The cubicle curtains flutter, someone walks past. They don't come in. *C'mon Harriet, at least shift the pan to stop its digging.* I raise my hips; electric white-flashing pain shoots up and down my right side. Another attempt. I'm breathing hard.

Thirty minutes. I've pushed the pan to one side but now it's biting at an angle. I try to give it another shove but I'm out of energy.

'Elsa?' I whisper.

Nothing.

'Elsa?'

I won't say it any louder. Mr Mohammed is talking to someone; all is quiet from Elsa's corner. My eyes flick to the river tributaries in the ceiling, and search for the moored boat. But today the water has dried up. The ground is caked dry. No boat. No journeys. In spite of the cubicle curtains, I feel as exposed as I had done at boarding school:

'Buck-up, New Fore*tht*! Get your*thelvth* to the bathroom, pronto!'

It's seven o'clock and lights-out is at half-past. Miss Brandon, standing in the dormitory doorway, hand on hip, is my favourite matron. We began Rookesbury on the same day, and she gets homesick too. I've watched tears sneak out from beneath the dab of her tissue. And when she's sad, a blotch, red as a clown's nose, appears at the top of each cheek as if she has coloured it in with her mum's lipstick. 'No running! And *th*ingle file!' she shouts after the fifteen of us. The bathroom is off the main corridor that leads to Senior End and is right by the Treatment area, where we go if we're not feeling well. There are no doors anywhere. Everyone can see everything. Tasha Edwards had a boil on her bottom, and every evening for a week she had to bend over a chair while Mrs Burroughs pricked it with a needle to get the poison out. Mrs B chatted to teachers and the older girls as they passed by; Tasha kept smiling – pyjama trousers heaped at her ankles – but it was a smile that looked as if it had been borrowed from someone else. There's a smell of soapy water and wet cork bath mats as we find our pegs and swap the two flannels and towel for our dressing gowns. It's a stand-up wash tonight; baths are every other night. The others are quickly naked, running taps, and the warm water steams up their mirrors. Lucy L has already got breasts and a triangle of very curly dark hair at the top of her legs that does not match the straight, light brown hair on her head; she's laughing with Julia and Vicky because the three of them are pretending to be robots washing. I'm still at the pegs, fishing soap and a toothbrush out of my *101 Dalmatians* wash-bag.

'Harriet Mercer! Get a move on!' shouts Mrs B from Treatment.

Another look around and I shrug off the turquoise fleecy dressing gown that Nom made me and cloak myself in my towel.

One basin left. I soap and rinse and flannel-squeeze with the hand that is not holding the towel. Nearly finished. Left foot in the basin, water trickles over the edge, I wash between my toes.

'Harriet! What *is* this nonsense?' Mrs B has ripped the cape from my back; I stumble backwards, and lose my balance. She holds the towel with the tips of her fingers, by its very edge, as if it had fallen into a cowpat. '*How many* times have I told you to leave it on the peg until you've *finished* washing?' Her glass eye gleams at me whilst the normal one swivels round to the other girls. 'What do you have that no one else has? A baboon's backside?' There's tittering and my face is baboon-bottom red as I get up from the floor trying to join in the laughter.

How can a blunt plastic edge scald?

Fluff on my cheek, I brush it away. But it's wetness, not fluff. Tears. They don't stop.

I reach for my phone. It's the first time I've made a call since I've been here.

'Hello.' My mother answers on the third ring.

'Hello, Harriet?'

'Hi.'

'Are you alright?'

'Mm no mm ...'

'What is it?'

'It hurts.'

'What hurts?'

'The bedpan.'

'Have you buzzed for someone?'

'Yes.'

'How long ago?'

'They're busy.'

'How long ago?'

'About forty minutes.'

'Forty minutes?'

'Yes.'

'Right. I'm going to phone the ward. Okay?'

'Sorry to moan.'

'You shouldn't have waited so long to call me. Someone will be with you very soon. I promise.'

And it is only a few minutes before Josey, a Filipino sister, slips in through a gap in the cubicle curtains.

'What you do, worry your ma on telephone? You must use buzzer, isn't it?' she says, snapping on rubber gloves.

'I buzzed, twice.'

'You keep trying then, okay?' She lifts the sheet and with very little effort pulls the pan away; all at once my body relaxes.

'You okay now?' A sigh skates in and out of those three words. She pulls open the cubicle curtains. Elsa is asleep, newspaper resting on her belly, a corner of it in her hand; Mr Mohammed's bed is empty.

*

A nutritionist drops by to prescribe some specially calorie-loaded snacks. The strawberry jelly is a sickly opaque pink and bears zero resemblance to the translucent rabbits that quiver and wobble at a five-year-old's party; the milkshake is a liquefied version of its partner-in-crime. Their chemical sweetness gags each one of my taste buds and I'm unable to keep either of them down. One morning my mother appears briefly with a thermos flask, *Thought you might like to try some of this for lunch*. The unmistakable aroma of her homemade chicken soup wafts from the flask before I've finished unscrewing its cap, and all at once I'm sitting at our dining table. On a tablemat is a blue ceramic bowl, by its side a spoon. My feet flex at the carpet's softness; a whippeting nose nudges my leg, and I stroke Harvey's velvet ears, his eyes – rimmed with Cleopatra's eyeliner – are beseeching; I say, *No. Not at the table*. I hear the washing machine and birds singing, and the distant slam of a car door. I take a spoonful of soup. But here and now, I neck it down directly from the thermos. *Looks good, Toots*, says Mr Mohammed; *Easy, girl! Go easy*, from Elsa. But I can't stop. It's hot though not too hot, and the layers of flavour are synaesthetic, like swallowing a song, lyrics, chords and voice all streaming down my throat. I taste my mother's love and drain the flask as if it were the dregs of a pint of Guinness, dwelling on the inner warmth of this first meal in four weeks. After a few minutes, an unmistakable churning somersaults the pit of my stomach and the sick bowl is ill prepared for the torrent of liquid that geysers back out of me. *Oh you, twit! You weren't meant to guzzle the lot ... you should've taken just small sips, and made it last*, says my mother when she returns that afternoon. *I told her, Elly. I did, didn't I Harriet?* says Elsa. *Yes*, I groan, the soup still repeating on me.

Getting ready for night-time. I reach forward to the table to check everything is at hand: phone, tissues, ginger ale, lip balm, pineapple chunks and sick-box. There's a rubbery squeal of wheel at the ward entrance.

It's Naomi.

She parks her wheelchair alongside my bed.

'Hiya!' Naomi says, her cheeks beatific, like a cherub's. 'How are you, love? I've been worried for you.' She's wearing the same cotton nightie; it drapes over the front of her chair, disguising the absence of both legs. Faith's face gusts through my mind on an odour of fish and chips, and melted cheese.

'Better, thanks,' I say, smiling hard.

'Good, good.' She's looking around, and grins at Elsa and Mr Mohammed. 'It's nice and quiet in here.'

'How ... how are you?' I remember my manners.

'On my way for a ciggy, of course, but I wanted to stop by and say cheerio cos I'm being discharged tomorrow. Home sweet home, can't wait,' she says, pulling her errant nightie sleeve back up her shoulder.

'Great news.' *Home:* eight miles from hospital. I revisit the sounds and textures of home that the soup evoked, but the picture has blurred as if it has been left out in the rain.

'Yup, they've stabilised it ... the kidney. But it'll be taken out if I don't mend my habits.' She smacks her left hand as if she were admonishing a child.

'Faith?' I ask. Naomi shakes her head and shifts in the wheelchair.

'Didn't you hear? She's been moved to a side room.'

'Oh.' Relief honeys my voice.

'Anyways, you take care of yourself.'

'And you.'

Naomi wheels out of the ward with a cheery wave.

Elsa's agog.

'Gawd! Look at her, happy as bleedin' Larry! I shan't complain now if they lop off me leg. At least I'll have the other one. But she'll catch her death, she will ... going out for a fag dressed like that,' says Elsa. 'You should see them all out there. At the front of the hospital. By the fountain, all puffing away.' She rolls her eyes. 'You don't smoke, do you, darlin'?'

Emily and I are supposed to be sweeping the stretch of pavement that leads down to Nom's bungalow but our brooms lie idle: instead, we're sitting on the kerb with freshly plucked lilac leaves on our knees; we roll the damp, heart-shaped leaves into one another. Then, back on our feet, we plan the afternoon's bike ride; cigarettes pinched between forefinger and middle finger, as we – hand on hip – affect the poses of Lauren Bacall and Bette Davis, and inhale deeply, casually blowing the occasional smoke ring until either the unlit leaves fall apart, or Daddy bellows at us, *There'll be no lunch until you've finished.*

'Lilac leaves.'

'Get on with you!' Elsa manoeuvres out of bed, toothbrush in hand.

The leaf cigarettes were stronger at Lampeter:

Don't stop, don't stop. Not here. Please. It's three o'clock in the morning and my car is bunny-hopping along the lane that winds down to Lampeter from Llanfair Clydogau. I've just left Jem's – it was a pretty typical evening, everyone sprawled in front of the fire, a few wood-sorties into the spinney behind his house, Pete and Jess jamming to John Martyn, plenty of chat, tea and toast, and a couple or ten telescopic reefers. *Come on, just a bit further. Don't wanna be stranded out here on my own.* Shapes stagger out from the hedgerow, and darkness etches them in shades of blue and black; they morph into wolfish figures and shrink back behind an overhanging tree; a yellow eye – *no it's a leaf, silly* – dancing in the beam of headlights; *Talk Talk* stutters in the cassette player and the car eventually gulps into town. Past the Co-op on the right, up Bryn Road, past The Newbridge, and Conti's on the corner, into the high street, and I notice that my knuckles are white on the steering wheel as if my tightened grip alone has drawn us this far. *Only another two and a half miles to go.*

But scarcely out of Lampeter we finally judder to a halt. I have very neatly broken down outside *Heddlu*, the Police Station. I turn the ignition; the car jumps forward and then cuts out.

In spite of the time, and Lampeter's next-to-zero crime rate, the station door pushes open, and behind the counter, sitting at a desk, is a police officer peering at me over a mug of tea.

'Hello,' I say, noting the signage on the counter: *Duty Sergeant: Alun Owen.*

'Bore da,' he says with a fleck of irony. 'How may I help yuer?'

'Yes, I'm sorry to trouble you. It's my car, I've …'

'Broken down, is it?'

'Um yes … just outside, actually.' My *t*'s sound stand-up-tall ostentatious.

Sergeant Owen is already reaching for his helmet from the top of a rather dilapidated looking filing cabinet. He puts it on and picks up a torch the size of a portable television. I follow him back out of the station and shiver. The fire seems like hours ago.

'There's nice … a Morris Minor, and half-timbered to boot.' He runs a finger along the car's woodwork and then walks round it as if he were admiring a racehorse.

'The engine keeps cutting out, perhaps it's the spark plugs?'

'Let's have a look, shall we? Pop up the bonnet, Bach.' I get in the car and root around above the footwell; I find the little lever and give it a tug. Sergeant Owen props the bonnet open, 'Yuer couldn't come and hold the torch, Bach?' I jump out of the driver's seat and shine the torch over the engine.

'They don't make them like this anymore,' he says, fiddling with various wires and connections. 'They can go at a tidy lick, mind.' He's right. My beloved green mean machine goes best at 70mph on the M4 back to London. He fiddles a bit more. 'Right. Start her up then.' I get back in the driver's seat, and put the torch on the passenger's side and turn the key. The moggy splutters into action. 'Give it welly, Bach.' He closes the bonnet. I rev it up, the engine sounds like a tank when it's at full throttle. 'There yuer are then, it was a loose wire.'

'That's amazing!' I gush. 'Thank you so much. And I'm sorry to have disturbed ...'

'How far have yuer got to go, Bach?'

'Oh really not far. A couple of miles.'

'Well now, I think it'd be prudent for me to give her a quick test drive.' *Oh, how I could swim up the length of that Welsh 'r'.* 'See, I wouldn't want yuer breaking down again.'

'I'm sure it's not necessary, you've been very kind,' I say, snapping back from his voice.

'Nonsense, Bach. Out yuer hop!'

I get out of my car and the sergeant takes off his helmet and slides, with some difficulty, behind the wheel.

'Duw, duw it must be twenty years since I've driven a Morris Minor.' It is only when he rests his helmet next to the television-sized torch that I notice how every nook and cranny of the front of the car is illuminated. Including the open glove compartment behind the steering wheel where my colourful tobacco tin nestles next to a small purple hash pipe, and the roach-ends in the footwells that have over spilled the ashtray. Sergeant Owen pulls the seat belt across his not inconsiderable stomach and adjusts the mirror. 'Just a few minutes, Bach.'

I stand outside the unlocked police station and watch my torchlit car disappear – like a shooting star – up Llanwnen Road; I hear the rumbling *parp-parp* as Sergeant Owen changes gear to take a corner. And another. It's freezing and this biker's jacket doesn't have pockets. But what have I been thinking? He's definitely going to spot the pipe. And if he opens the tin, he'll find that stubby bit of hash. Why did I leave it there? I usually keep it in my bra. I could get done for this big time. Last week someone was fined 200 quid for having less than an eighth on them. It was all over the *Carmarthen Journal*. Shit.

It's almost ten minutes before the circular headlamps swing back into view.

'Good as gold, thar wun.' Sergeant Owen pats the bonnet. 'She runs a treat, I must say.' And he returns his helmet to his head.

'Really?' My heart is leaping; I scrutinise his face for suspicion. It's poker straight.

'Absolutely. Now where is it yuer live?'

'Pentrebach.' I try to say it as nonchalantly as possible, and slip back into the still warm driver's seat.

'Ah, up at Jones's farm, is it?' *Uh-oh.*

I nod.

He nods.

'Thank you, again,' I say, my foot on the accelerator.

'Not at all, Bach.' And Sergeant Owen winks at me as I drive off.

'That's me done,' says Elsa, back from the bathroom and making herself as comfortable as she can in bed. 'Night, all.'

'Sleep well,' I say.

'Good night, my friends.' Mr Mohammed's voice has already hunkered down.

Weighted with tiredness, I allow my eyes close to orangey red light. One brick, then two, the wall builds itself. Cement dribbles. The bricks become honeycombed, and the holes enlarge. No. My eyes flick open and I hear a muffled conversation at the nurses' station and I drift back to Lampeter. And then to the faded ink of my evacuated, thirteen-year-old father's letter to his own father:

'Springfield'
Wycliffe College
Lampeter
Cardiganshire
Wales
Great Britain
21st March, 1944

... Last Sunday I went for a walk with my friend, a Belgian boy. We were going up Llanwnen Road when suddenly he got cold. So I suggested he toddle back and get his jacket and said I would wait for him. About five minutes after he had gone I looked around for something to do. My eyes alighted on a field of lambs with their mothers (God strife the man who harms them). I had an idea! For I noticed how often they made a mistake when they wanted a drink of milk. It would be an experiment in animal psychology, I would pretend to be one of their mothers! I jumped over the fence and got on my hands and knees and bahaaed like a sheep. After noticing how their bahaas varied, I got hold of a nice bahaa and repeated it in an encouraging way for some time. (No doubt the passers-by thought me a barmy college boy!) To my pleasure and delight a pair of twin lambs skipped up to me. But when they touched me with their noses they realized I was not one of them. Very interesting. I have thus proved: - they were colour blind or poorly sighted, or they were extremely inquisitive which I think is most likely …

I imagine floor-to-ceiling curtains hanging before me; I part them, and walk into veil after flowing veil until I am in a tunnel that might be a silkworm's cocoon. I slip through its satiny layers, losing all awareness of time; in the distance I see stained glass, and as I get closer it's as if I'm looking through a kaleidoscope. Chinks of colour stretch into expanses and as I stare, they open out onto road, field and sky. And I see that fence, raindrops cling to it for dear life; others glisten, sewn into strands of sheep's wool, caught on the wire. I climb over and join the boy version of my father. He's getting up from his hands and knees, brushes down his long grey shorts and runs a hand through his thatch of hair. The lambs skip, and suckle their mothers who chomp on, in the ocean of grass. The boy watches them intently and then turns round. I'm standing slap-bang in front of him, but he looks straight through me and lifts his arm to wave at a fast approaching ant figure, the Belgian boy. I scour the blue-grey-greens of his irises for clues, and tiptoe the edge of his pupils, and look down into their wells of darkness, hunting for any trace of the demons that are lying in wait.

Coughing returns me to the ward with a jolt. I whoop for breath; the retching intensifies and just as I think I will suffocate, I cough up a mass of stringy pale green gloop. These choking attacks have replaced the vomiting. Afterwards, I sip some ginger ale, and revert to breathing in time with first Elsa and then Mr Mohammed, who remain thankfully undisturbed, while focusing on the objects on my table. In addition to the regulars, there's a spiralbound hardback notebook; its cover is white and patterned with brightly coloured butterflies, their bodies textured and glittery. Inside, scrawled in biro, is *HARRIET'S HOSPITAL THOUGHTS. You are in the best hands. I will see you soon, fit and well. Fxxx* The unlined paper is heavyweight, begging for ink. Normally my pen would be poised, nib a millisecond away from greeting the whiteness as if I'd happened upon a deserted beach. But the glare shining up from the blankness is numbing; it does not provoke any urge in me: holding a pen would be as heavy as a newspaper. Finlay delivered the notebook to my mother while I was in HDU; *He phones me several times a week for a progress report*, she tells me. The crosses in his message siren alarm, like the fear in Amelia's eyes: Finlay never signs off with a kiss.

The night limps on, with me tucked under its arm.

'It's just a little something, dear.' Mrs Mohammed has been rummaging in her capacious bag, and hands me a nest of tissue paper. Beneath the wrapping, I trace a cubed, knobby structure. The tissue falls away, unveiling a tea light candleholder, encircled by rows of plump red and amber glass beads alternately suspended on copper wire.

'It's beautiful,' I say, straight into her hazelnut eyes. 'Thank you.' My words do not seem to balance her colossal kindness. She nods.

'Think of the lightness,' she says with her gentle smile, 'when you go home.' And she clasps my fingers.

Home is still a rainbow's length away. A few days after the bedpan incident, my mother reminds me of the health insurance taken out last year. *Charing Cross has a private wing on the fifteenth floor ... just think, your own room*, she says raising her eyebrows in question. Reluctantly, I agree to her to investigating the possibility.

'Why the hesitation?' she asks.

'Mm ... feel guilty.'

'Guilty?! Whatever for?'

'The NHS, it's saved my life,' I say, 'and them,' I look in the direction of Mr Mohammed and then to Elsa, 'they help so much.'

'I know, Harriet. But look at it like this, you'll be freeing-up a much needed bed.'

In any event, my team is initially averse to the idea. *You're not out of the woods yet; if anything goes wrong you're better off down here.* Behind the scenes my mother does not give up. And after some wrangling they come back to me: *Okay, Harriet, Mr Winkler has agreed to look after you on the fifteenth floor.* Mr Winkler. I haven't seen him since Critical Care, although I've looked for his face every day in ward rounds.

Things happen fast: the morning after the decision has been made, a nurse comes to my bedside, with a trolley laden with alarming items: rubber gloves, a plastic measuring jug, a needleless syringe, big dressing and a bedpan. She closes the cubicle curtains, checks the ID on my wrist, and asks me my name.

'Thanks, Harriet,' she says. 'I've been requested to remove your catheter today.'

'Right.' I utter this as if I was expecting the procedure, but no one had told me.

'Yes, it'll be much better if you move upstairs without it.' She's put on gloves and is emptying the catheter bag into the jug. 'Don't worry, it won't hurt, you'll probably just feel a little tug. It might take a few days for your body to adjust, though ... how long have you had it in ... about a month?' I nod. '... yes, these things can take time.'

My euphoria shrivels as I think of all the implications attached to *adjust*.

But my body *adjusts* seamlessly.

*

I'm hunched over the Zimmer frame; it's the first time I've been on my feet since the nosebleed. I straighten up as much as I can; it's my stomach that's dragging me down.

'Are you feeling dizzy?' Sasha the physio asks.

'I'm okay,' I say, blinking away the black spots that are floating in and out of my vision.

'Just relax, and get your bearings,' she says. But I want to get on with this and remember the instructions given to me on Faith's ward: I lift the frame, placing it a hand's length in front of me. Right foot, first. *Legs, you are still so leaden.* Then left. Lift the frame. Right foot ...

'I can see you've done this before,' says Sasha, wheeling the IV stand at my side.

'She can't wait to leave us, can she, Mr M?' Elsa teases.

'Who can blame her when she's off to posher climes?' says Mr Mohammed.

The affection in their voices spurs me further.

'Okay, let's turn back now.' The physio puts a hand on my shoulder.

'To the door,' I say. When I do turn round, sunlight is streaming through the windows. Lift. Left foot. Right foot. Lift. They are not fluid movements. It feels as if my weighted stomach and legs are connected by wire, and the pull of each step threatens to cut me in half. But these are steps towards home. I know it.

Chapter Twelve

Scar

The wound is the place where the Light enters you

– Rumi

Last year, in January 2018, I helped dismantle the jewellers in Richmond where I had worked on and off for the previous twelve years. It was one of those shops made daunting by the bell customers needed to ring in order to enter. Once inside it was Zen calm, as if you'd left the high street a million miles away and stepped into someone's rather beautiful and faded front room. The jewellery we sold rarely moved me, but I was very fond of my colleagues, we rubbed along like a happy, dysfunctional family, and during the quieter periods I could write. Susan had owned the shop for almost thirty years when her Parkinson's was diagnosed and the premises needed to be sold in order to pay for her care home costs. She'd been poorly for a while and was finally admitted to hospital. I was amazed, when I visited her, to find that out of all the wards of Charing Cross, a huge teaching hospital, she was on 4 South – where I had stayed with Mr Mohammed and Elsa – and in the exact bed space that I occupied when she had visited me.

Back at the shop, Nye – manager, the son Susan never had – and I spent days separating her possessions from shop paraphernalia as if in the aftermath of her death. It was a particularly harrowing task knowing that the home Susan had been transferred to, from Charing Cross, was, for all its luxury, largely windowless; indeed, nothing like a home. On one of these grim sorting days the bell rang. And in the slow-motion seconds of me opening the door, I recognised the man standing there and watched him study my face with incredulity flickering in his eyes as his mind, our minds, rewound the spool of decades: *Harriet?* he said. The last time I had seen him was as a fourteen-year-old schoolgirl waiting for the number 9 bus at Barnes Bridge. He'd seemed ancient to me then, although he can only have been in his mid-twenties. I remembered his Aberdeenshire accent, and that our conversations had been interesting, for we had chatted on many a morning. *It's Gerry*, he said, *do you remember?*

He said he was passing through Richmond when he noticed Susan's had closed down, and had wondered whether we had any fittings that might be appropriate for the shop he was soon to open. And as he spoke, it came back to me the nature of those conversations that fascinated me all those years ago, the cool stories of St Martins and of how he became a jewellery designer. A few days later he left a message about a couple of items he had enquired after, and to see if I'd be interested in helping him get his new shop up and running. I called back intending to thank him and say that I was looking for a more book-orientated job. But when he answered his phone the coincidences continued to roll – he was having coffee with one of my sister's best friends – and several weeks later I changed my mind.

Gerry's workbench is at the back of the shop. I watch his jewellery being made from sketched design to finished piece; a ring, for example, set with a Paraiba tourmaline the colour of the Aegean Sea, it's gold shank striped with inlaid platinum, inspired by Tutankhamun's heqa sceptre. The shop itself is more like a gallery with all the pieces – dear or less so – given space to breathe. Everything is tucked in the safe at night, and one of my favourite pieces to put out again in the morning is not jewellery but a silver beaker named Kevin, made by the Bristol-based award-winning silversmith, Elizabeth Auriol Peers. I unwrap Kevin from his tissue paper, releasing him from night, and hold him a while, my hand enveloping the cold metal, fingers nestling under the ridge that flows into the beaker's protuberance. Customers remark upon this unexpected feature, because if you look at the vessel from behind, it's not visible – the beaker appears a sculptural and gloriously tactile piece but without hint of particular poignancy. Some customers imagine the pointy, textured protuberance to be a fox's head, and others a beak. Depending on their disposition, I tell them the story. The protuberance is part of the scar on Kevin's hand, suffered when he rescued a child from a burning house; Kevin is a fireman. When you examine the 'fox's head', light catches the texture of pitted skin, and the pulled-tight wrinkles of the actual scar: to create this, Auriol Peers took an alginate mould of the negative space in Kevin's hand from which she made a lost wax casting in silver, and it was then set into the body of the beaker she'd hand-raised.

Asymmetry is what I like, to celebrate the fat and folds of the human form, its curves and crevices. I love scars, there's always a story behind a scar. I'm drawn to the melted skin of burns victims, says the silversmith. It was meeting James Partridge OBE, founder of the charity Changing Faces, that inspired Auriol Peers's line of research into facial disfigurement and distortion. Partridge received 40 per cent burns to his face, upper body and hands from a car accident as an eighteen-year-old and required extensive reconstructive plastic surgery. His bravery, how he turned his life around (and subsequently the lives of others through the charity) after such a life-altering trauma, has had a profound effect on

Auriol Peers. While working with fellow silversmiths in Holland's 'silver city', Schoonhoven, she began designing her statement piece, the 280mm-high hand-raised vase of a head, named James. She's keen to emphasise that it's not a replica of Partridge's face although it is based on his scarring; *I was particularly fascinated by the tubular skin graft that was grown down his back. The skin was used over his cheek and chin. I use it as the 'nose' of my piece.* She works freely and draws the markings and movements on the metal as she deepens and manipulates the silver. It reminds her of the crude pen markings that the surgeons make on their patients before plastic surgery or operations. James has been exhibited but so far, she has declined all offers, the sentimental value of the vase is too high. I tell Lizzie that I'm sorry we haven't sold Kevin yet; unsaid and selfishly, I'm relieved. It's a privilege to feel the beaker take on the warmth of my hands before I place it on the glass shelf, to admire the scarring and remember the act of selflessness that caused it. *Well, scars are hard things to sell*, she says. They really shouldn't be, though. Because through her beautiful works, Auriol Peers challenges our perceptions of disfigurement.

A scar is a timeline, beginning with the event that caused the wound, and ending with completion of the physical healing process. There are, of course, numerous types of wound,[51] and while their resulting scars fade over time with the help of soothing oils and ointments, the length of time it takes to heal psychologically depends on several variables: the trauma of the wound event; the length of time the wound itself takes to heal; the severity of any disability that the combined wound and scar has on the individual's life; and on its appearance. Everyone has been wounded, if only by a mosquito, and most people have

---

51   From those incurred by minor accidents to those of routine surgeries, burns, acute wounds of gangland stabbings, self-inflicted wounds, chronic wounds (that require complex wound management systems in order to heal) and invisible wounds.

the odd scar or if they don't, know someone who has one. My angiomyolipoma, although no longer the size of a rugby ball, has the dimensions of an orange. Leeched to my kidney, its yellow fattiness blobs around and yawns its presence: I can be doing something completely innocuous like getting out of the bath or bending to pick up the whippet's water bowl when I'm hit in my right side so unexpectedly and sharply that I yelp with indignation and familiarity as if rebuking an offending relative standing close by. These twinges may occur only a couple of times a week. Matt Winkler, the consultant urologist who saved my life, monitors the angiomyolipoma at regular intervals and he's relaxed about this residual and minute discomfort, *It's scar tissue,*[52] he says, *you'll always have it. And it'll always remind you.* It has also bemused me; I've felt sheepish over the years for worrying about something that hasn't left a visible scar.

I'm fortunate that the discomfort from my internal scarring is minor and does not affect my day-to-day life in any way. Matt Winkler's expertise, when he's not diagnosing rare kidney tumours, is prostate laparoscopic surgery ... *massive three- or four-hour-long operations, afterwards you can't see a thing, there's barely a mark and yet the surgery can render you infertile ... invisible scars – internal scars that impact daily living, one's social life, working life, walking the dog life, sex life – are probably the worst scars.* The major benefit of laparoscopic surgery is that it's minimally invasive, and that its results are accordingly aesthetically pleasing. Yet implicit in Matt's words is the suggestion that the mechanical and psychological repercussions of such surgery can be further devastating when there isn't the landmark of a physical scar; that although scars are perceived as unsightly, they are a valuable point of reference. A close friend who has undergone breast cancer

---

52 Caused by two embolisations of the angiomyolipoma.

surgeries, and three open-heart operations where the incisions left a fiery red line from the base of her neck to her stomach, wonders whether others find her scarring *repulsive*, but she wears her heart scar as a *badge of honour, or badge of achievement*. It reminds her of what it took for her to remain alive.

As an English Literature undergraduate, I sat behind Lisa in lectures. Lisa sang in a band; she was vivacious, always smiling, wore ripped 501s and a Mod-ish '60s shade of pink lipstick. I also remember her having this fabulous long blond ringletty hair that she'd flick back, looking effortlessly glamorous. Her hair cascaded over the back of her seat in those English lectures, and instead of doodling I took an immature delight in inking the tips of it goth black. A couple of years ago we reunited via Facebook. I was horrified to learn that she'd been the victim of a gas explosion. As I read her words on Messenger, my mind tore ahead, with images of her crouched down in a warehouse on some industrial site, with its windows blast out and shards of glass covering her ... it took a few minutes for my brain to absorb what I was reading, that it had happened at home. It didn't make sense that something like this could happen at home or to the girl that I remembered Lisa to be. But of course, these things can and do happen to anyone. At the time of the explosion she was a teacher, she'd returned home from school on 18 July 2007, at about 17.30, and noticed that both her sofa-hugging cats were sitting outside in the front garden:

I remember pausing at the door because I thought it was an unusual thing for them to do. As soon as I walked into the cottage, I heard a loud hissing sound and went into the kitchen to see what was causing it. I thought it was the washing machine. I walked straight over to it, put my bags down, put my keys on the worktop and turned to the cooker. By this time I was standing directly in front of the cooker. I don't really remember exactly how it ignited, whether I touched a knob or whether my keys and bags caused some sort of spark. I just recall amazing blooms of bright orange fire completely enveloping my head and body. The volume and pitch of the explosion was like nothing I had ever heard before. I shielded my face with my hands and then calmly realised that I was about to die. I didn't feel frightened or scream at this point. I was then thrown up and across the room, inside the fireball, landing up against the wall, on top of a worktop the opposite side of the room. I felt the heat of the fire on my back and head and climbed down from the worktop and ran out of the cottage. The front door had been blown apart as had the ceiling … I heard my voice as if it was from someone else, high pitched, screaming … my hands and ankles looked odd. I had never seen skin look like that before; it looked pure white and felt as if it was still on fire.

Lisa managed to gain access to her neighbour's house and douse herself with water, and the ambulance crew continued to spray her on the way to hospital. This proved critical, because although her hair was burnt off and she suffered flash burns to her face, second and third degree burns to her wrists and ankles, and endured months of her hands being covered with dressings (that needed regularly changing, an agonising process), while her ankles resembled *raw meat* and were difficult to move, her physical recovery was remarkable.

I never ever take my face, hair, hands and ankles for granted … I seem to take a ridiculous amount of selfies and I think I am forever celebrating how I look compared to how I thought I would. I'm proud of the physical scars that are there because they do remind me of what I had to go through to get to this point. I survived by pure luck.

She believes it was the rubble-filled thick walls of her 1740s Welsh long cottage that saved her life. They wobbled but didn't crumble. The explosion, though, blew 40 tonnes of roof off the purlins, and:

All floors were literally blown upwards and snapped and the interior walls blown in. The doors and windows including frames were blown out ... The only thing to burn was me as the force of the explosion created a fire ball which used up all of the gas but did not set the cottage ablaze.

The cottage's rebuilding took a year, the work running parallel with stages of her recovery. It seemed that as her body was busy repairing itself, the demolition of her own interior walls became more apparent.

The biggest issue I had to come to terms with was my identity. I didn't look, feel or react the way I had before the accident. I didn't have my possessions or live in my home. I didn't relate to people or situations in the same way. I didn't feel that I was a 'coper' anymore. I had always been carefree, a risk taker and someone who took charge when things got tough ... Therapy made me contemplate who I really was when everything around me appeared to have physically and mentally changed. Six months after the accident I was diagnosed with Post Traumatic Stress Disorder. I think the diagnosis helped me forgive myself for changing so significantly in such a short space of time ... The long-term scars may not be visible but impact on my life in many ways. I am now a loner and need to spend a lot of time by myself, but can often feel lonely. I react to stress by being short tempered, have had panic attacks or shut down and need to sleep. I don't trust people easily and feel anxious in public places. I'm plagued by catastrophic thinking and often feel an overwhelming sense of imminent doom. I am overprotective of my son and sometimes struggle to keep perspective. But, in spite of all of that I firmly believe it was the best thing to happen to me. I have much more compassion and empathy for those who face or have faced trauma. Since it happened, I've worked with military veterans who also have PTSD and gained a more profound understanding of my brother who has chronic PTSD following active service in Iraq. I have the gift of gratitude and feel incredibly lucky to have survived and now make sure that I live my life the way I want to instead of how others think I should.

I felt both inspired and pained by Lisa's experience, of what she has had to endure, still endures, and the incredible style with which she has survived. Her words though also made me feel less of a freak. I empathised with her catastrophic thinking: I'm forever scared that something appalling will befall those that I'm closest to, that any unfamiliar pain is the symptom of another life-threatening illness; the way my body viscerally reacts when I hear a siren. It is a joyous thing to have your life saved, your senses are recalibrated and you experience nature and colour and music as if for the first time; you enjoy everything and everyone more intensely: it maddens me, then, that I allow the catastrophic thinking to gate-crash this wondrous party. Lisa's experience also reminded me of Rumi's much quoted phrase, *The wound is the place where the Light enters you* ... and I share with her the perhaps odd-sounding view that I'm grateful my illness happened, gargoyles and all. It was the richest of life lessons.

Kevin, by Elizabeth Auriol Peers

Chapter Thirteen

'I'll be seeing ya, Darling.' Elsa waves the piece of paper on which my mother has written down my phone number.

'Keep strong, Toots. Missing your smile already!' Mr Mohammed pats my bed as it passes him.

'Bye,' I say. Something twists in my chest. *Have I thought this through?* I cannot imagine the past amount of time – *how long … ten days, two weeks?* – without their presence. *But where are the words to express my gratitude?*

Sister holds the lift doors open and the porter wheels me in backwards. My mother is pinioned to one side, weighted down with paraphernalia. Sister squeezes in on the other side, and presses 15 on the panel by her elbow.

'Doors closing.' The automated woman's voice is silkily sci-fi.

Cold hands. I slip them under the sheets. The lift jerks upwards, a rocket ascent that leaves my stomach behind and spins my head. My mother shrugs off her lift phobia and smiles at me, her chin cupped in leopard-faced orchid bloom. The floors flit by in neon pink … four … five … six … seven … eight … nine … like floodlit years: storeys and stories.

'Doors opening.'

Straight through swing doors. Quiet. No kitchen odours. The nurses' station. I spot Sister hand over the book of notes before she vanishes, as my bed speeds along a long blue corridor to the last room on 15 North.

The room is a gigantic window-filled space, about 15m square, a corner room jutting out over Hammersmith. A wannabe penthouse. Wall fixtures suggest that in another life it was a ward of three beds. But now there is just a solitary bed, an island on the sea of Aegean carpet, and the porter parks me up as close to it as can be. The light is searing.

'You couldn't get a better view of the Thames, Harriet!' my mother says, reading my mind and closing the blinds that are in my eyeline. 'It's panoramic! You can see Hammersmith Bridge, and right the way up to Barnes.' *Hammersmith Bridge, its creaks and groans ...* I crossed it every day, on the number 9 bus. I'd stand on its platform, hanging off the maypole, wind in my face, *hold on tight*, the conductor said, as the green of the bridge blurred past and I enjoyed the final swing onto the Broadway, where I leapt off early for the shortcut to secondary school.

My mother darts out of vision. 'Niiice bathroom,' she says, reappearing and pointing from whence she has come. She is a relative mile away.

'Hello there, I'm Maria and I'll be settling you in this afternoon.' The staff nurse has a smile to match the length of this room. 'First thing is to get you in this bed,' she says. 'Can you slide across for me?' It's more inelegant shuffle than slide. The bed feels firmer than the waterbed. Maria uses the remote control device to adjust the back so I'm sitting upright. 'A bit lower?' I ask.

'No sweetheart, we must keep them lungs clear,' she says, moving on to checking my dormant cannula. *Softness in her tone.* I bid silent farewell to my waterbed – *we've sailed some adventures, haven't we?* – as it disappears out of the room with the porter, and Maria. Once my mother has finished making sure all my essentials are near to hand, she leaves too; extolling her delight on the discovery of a minibar-type fridge in which she plans to store all sorts of tempting nutritional fancies. Her happiness at this simple thing makes me happy too; that she's having a break from worry.

And now, apart from the orchid – who seems to be preening its balletic branches, appreciative of a table all to itself – I am alone. Peace tents the room; billowing, rippling, and I breathe in, slowly. I no longer feel sick – at all. This is good. Tomorrow the physio will start properly and it'll be only a matter of days before I go home. Why, perhaps I'll even have breakfast tomorrow, and read a newspaper too. In this relaxed state I survey the new surrounding landscape. To my right is the doorway, and on my left another blue chair ... I find the continuity of this oddly reassuring. There's a television and radio overhead; four chairs and a table are positioned invitingly by the windows. The door to the bathroom is ajar. Tomorrow, I'll get there. The ceiling ... I search for new rivers to follow. A knock at the door, and I jump.

'Sorry to startle you,' says Mr Winkler, striding in, all smiles and dark suit.

'I'm very happy when my patients get this room,' he says, looking round approvingly.

'It *is* big.' *Can't you think of anything more meaningful to say – other than stating the obvious?*

'Yup. It was perfect for your predecessors. They sustained pretty major injuries in a car accident, they were here for months. Nice that they could be together. May I?' He gestures towards one of the chairs by the window and brings it over to the door side of my bed. 'It was a long haul, but they're fighting fit now.' He beams. 'Now, how are *you* feeling?'

'Much better,' I say.

'That's excellent.' He flicks through the clipboard of notes attached to the end of my bed. 'But you understand how serious your condition has been, in fact still is?' His own smile has left the building and his eyes really are a very piercing blue. I nod.

'It was quite a battle to have you moved up here. Because when you're very ill it *is* much safer to be with the NHS, you know? And you're still at high risk from a re-bleed ... so spike a fever of 37.5 and you'll be back down there.' Perhaps it's his sudden sternness, but out of nowhere, and to my mortification, tears start rolling down my cheeks.

'Oh dear. I don't mean to upset you.' He passes me tissues from the over-bed table, concern and embarrassment colouring his face. 'But you need to know how it is.' His tone is gentler.

'Yes, of course,' I say, wiping the tears away. 'Sorry, I don't mean to cry.'

'And you *will* require careful monitoring once you do get home – any nausea or hint of fever and you must call an ambulance ...'

'*When* can I go home?' It sounded as if home was imminent.

'We have to play it by ear but I should think in a couple of weeks.'

'A couple of weeks?' My voice tumbles, like dominoes.

'The longer you go without a re-bleed, the more comfortable we'll feel. And we need to continue with our programme of stabilisation – get you a bit stronger and mobile.'

The quietness, after he has left, has a different complexion to the earlier sense of peace; it is pitted with the fear that I thought I'd left on the fourth floor.

'Are you okay, sweetheart? The doctor said you been upset now?' Maria is back.

'I'm fine ... I was being silly.' The balled-up tissue is still in my hand.

'How about something to eat?' Her voice is hushed as if there are others in the room that she doesn't want to disturb.

'There's pineapple in the fridge,' I say.

'What about your dinner?'

'No, just pineapple, please.'

'We're gonna have to feed you up,' she says, fetching the little Tupperware tub containing the fresh chunks. 'You know, a few years back, I was proper poorly. Like you, girl. I lost so much weight I made a skelly look fat. And now look at me!' Maria gives a gusty laugh and smoothens her straining uniform.

'Did it take long ... for you to get better?'

'Long enough. But you wait. Time is a superb thing. When I look back at them months, it was only seconds, really. You'll see. But you gotta eat. Cos an empty bag cyna stand up.' And she sticks a thermometer in my mouth.

'Anyway, I got meself better – and it was me that did that, with God's help of course – the doctors can't do the recuperation bit for you. Remember that, girl. Then I got me this job and enough money to bring over my child. I hadn't set eyes on her for over three years.'

'How old is she?' I ask through the thermometer.

'Maya? She's thirteen now. She's a good girl. Conscientious, you know. I worry when me shifts finish late or when I work nights. Because of the neighbourhood. But she just bolts the door when she gets home from school, makes herself something to eat and settles down to her homework. Yes, thank the Lord ... my Maya studies hard. She gonna do well, of that I have no fear.'

When I lie awake in the small hours, that is the image I play to myself over and over again. I follow navy-uniformed Maya with falling down socks into a lift decorated by Biker Boyz; on her blazer is the emblem of Sacred Heart School, and when she smiles at the old man who gets off the floor before hers, her lips part into her mother's smile. Out of the lift she trails her fingertips along the railings until she reaches a mustard front door. And just as Maria says, the first thing she does when she lets herself in is to shoot the hefty, cold-looking bolt across the door and then she kicks off her shoes and hangs up her blazer. In the kitchen, she dumps her schoolbag on the table and reaches for a tumbler from a high-up shelf on the sideboard. She pours herself milk, whisking in a spoonful of strawberry Nesquik powder until there's a froth of pink popping bubbles. And then she spreads a slice of bread with peanut butter and sits down at the table with her sandwich and milkshake. She pulls an exercise book from her bag, a pen from her pencil case, and starts to write, occasionally looking up at a photograph stuck to the fridge. A younger, maybe ten-year-old Maya stands in the middle of her proud-looking grandparents. Vibrant fringing of greenery frames the three happy faces and distracts from the thumbed edges of the photograph, and from the flat greys of the kitchen. Maya looks through a textbook; the flutter of each page turned is in time with the tick of the wall clock. I follow the minute hand take its laborious steps round the face until I realise that I've left Maya and am watching the clock on the wall ahead of me.

Three a.m. and any hope that sleep would be easier up here has come face-to-face with wide-awake reality. It's certainly quieter, but I am still sitting upright and the pillows and sheets continue their travels without me, and when I close my eyes it is only a millisecond before the backs of my eyes are alive with crumbling brick wall and hungry gargoyles. Emptiness shouts from the space that Mr Mohammed and Elsa could occupy, and silence squeals the absence of their night-time breathing.

Six a.m. and no vampire to start the day. *Last time*, I said to him yesterday when he had tapped the inside of my elbow and said *sharp scratch*; he had filled the phials, *Moving ward?* he'd whispered. I nodded, watching him label the sealed vacutainers of my blood.

'Thank you for always being gentle.'

'No problem. I hope you're better soon,' and he smiled, gave a grave little bow and wheeled his trolley on to Mr Mohammed.

At 7.30, I am brought a cup of tea and a bowl of Rice Crispies. In the normal world, I can't function without a hit of coffee to start the day. The breakfast sits on a tray.

The tray.

I race up the spiralled stairs of my mind – two at a time – to the gallery and a maze of images. But I know my way, and turn a few corners until I find the dream that I had in my twenties which now hangs with the subdued grandeur of a renowned painting.

Plastered creamy white walls bulge here and there. Exposed wooden beams, of a similar darkness to the floorboards, chunk across the ceiling. The leaded window is open and gauzy curtains, delicate as butterfly wings, flutter in the breeze. Facing the wall is a mahogany bed, and sitting against a tower of pillows is a man having breakfast from a tray that looks as if it has been carved from the same wood that bore the bed. He is eating a boiled egg. As the teaspoon nears his lips, a drop of yolk plummets, and smatters the white bed linen. An elongated orange beak pecks at toast fanning the eggcup, for next to the man nestles a swan, its neck bent towards him like a tulip stem; sheets ruckled against feathers. The man does not pay any attention to his companion. His face is devoid of any momentous feature or expression. Momentarily, that is, because his head suddenly shrinks a little and his hair lengthens until it curls into naked shoulders and his features refine, hatching through softening skin. Both arms stretch up high, a yawn, and the bedclothes fall away, and Venus de Milo breasts peek out. The tray remains miraculously balanced. And then the woman settles back against the pillows and sips her cup of tea, and the swan sleeks its head under a wing.

A sip of tea, *I've been looking forward to this all night*, the tannin is thick but not unpleasant. The metamorphosis remains an unanswered riddle no matter how many times I revisit the gallery. Rice Crispies crackle in the milk. Another sip of tea. And a spoonful of cereal. My mouth is in heaven with the chill of the milk after the warmth of the tea and alternating the sensations helps me finish half the bowl of cereal in spite of not being hungry. *The more you eat, the more strength you'll have … after all, an empty bag cyna stand up*, I chide. I asked the nurse that came to do my obs if Maria would be on duty, but was told to my dismay that she'd be taking ten days annual leave. *To your dismay, probably not Maya's, though*, I remind myself.

As on the other wards, a bowl of warm water together with clean gown and paper towels are put down on the over-bed table, alongside my soap, toothbrush, fennel toothpaste and deodorant. For a moment I allow myself to wallow in the privacy. And then I reach for the soap and hear myself gasp. In that split-second I'm dazzled by a recurrence of the zinc-white flash, and razor pain that slices back and forth through my right side and back. I slump against the pillows. I try again with the soap but the action leaves me cursing and hardly daring to move. Washing becomes a mission of working out minute movements that don't trigger the serrated sensations. It's not just washing that provokes the return of this monster, it seethes and foams each time I am helped to move the 18 inches from bed to chair, making it a forty-minute transition.

Chapter Fourteen

Passengers

As I walked up Parliament Hill the grass rippled beneath a pleasing breeze, and the London skyline gleamed with such clarity that it felt as if you could stretch over and prick your finger on the Shard. An elderly man sat on the bench ahead; it was his colourful garb – specifically his orange bucket hat and cerise shirt – and the Yorkshire Terrier on his lap that caught my eye. We exchanged pleasantries, acknowledged the view, and the beautiful June afternoon; he noticed my camera and commented on its vintage look and then I walked on, only to double back and enquire whether he would mind if I photographed them. *We'd be flattered, wouldn't we?* he said, stroking the dog's head. After we introduced ourselves, I looked through the viewfinder and found Jack's pale blue eyes contemplating me with gentle amusement. Yes, it was the broken nose and furrowed brow, and the contrast of his vibrant attire against the surrounding verdancy, and the tenderness he showed his wannabe Afghan Hound, Oscar, that would all combine to make a good picture. But it was something less visible that had compelled me to return to photograph them: Jack's hands were huge in relation to his slight stature, he gestured with pianist's fingers, and in this movement I had glimpsed, at his wrists, a long-sleeved black top under the buttoned-to-its-collar shirt. My gut read between the layers and sensed vulnerability shadowing his laid-back demeanour.

I took a couple of shots and as I snapped, it transpired that Jack and Oscar were on a farewell tour of their favourite places in London: the following week they would be moving to Brighton. Jack felt he knew London like the back of his hand; *there's still time to get to know somewhere else*, he said. He had been a bus conductor on the iconic double-decker Routemasters, and it's difficult indeed to imagine another occupation that would have afforded him a better insight into the city and its people. I could still remember several of the conductors, women and men who oversaw the number 9 – the bus I caught to school. Like their musical counterparts, they conducted an ensemble of varying voices, from infants to pensioners, from commuters to tourists, from drunks to divas, from descant to baritone. They were consummate multitaskers with eyes at the backs of their heads, and the balance of an Olympic skateboarder. They'd take fares, find change, give tickets, squeeze past standing passengers, yoyo up and down the stairs, stow dripping umbrellas, buggies and luggage, answer route enquiries, all while the bus was still moving and usually with a friendly word or two. Every school day, I'd race up to the top deck to see if my favourite seat at the front was free. *Ding ding*, the bell was pulled, the conductor's signal to the driver, and the old bus would lurch forward and I'd rub at the steamed-up window, to watch the street below, and listen to the hubbub of bus banter. Conductors possessed rough charm but were polished diplomats: they were maestros who owned their decks. *Ennnnnny more fares?* I mimicked their call, as familiar as birdsong, and Jack chuckled. *That's right*, he said.

'What did you enjoy most about being a conductor?' I asked. It was like meeting a childhood hero.

'The conversation, without a doubt, especially with the regular passengers. I fell in love with a passenger ... yes, I did ... Sue travelled my route for nearly three years. She was British Airways cabin crew, with her hair in a bun,' his hands flew up to gesticulate the sweep of chignon. 'She was immaculate; her uniform was always just so. We chatted. Because we had similar jobs, didn't we? Except hers was in the sky. We looked after people on their journeys.'

'That's a brilliant common denominator.'

'It was. We both loved our jobs. I fell for her, of course I did. But I was never going to be enough. For a gal like Sue. I was used to her absences, because she did long-haul. She'd always be back, blowing my mind with one exotic location or another. And then the absences stretched out a bit. Until one day, she told me her news. I wasn't surprised. She'd fallen in love with a pilot, you see. Of course she had. He had a lifestyle way out of my league. I understood. And she was so happy. I was pleased for her. But it didn't mean that I wasn't broken-hearted. It was the only time I've been in love. I never saw her again, not since she got off my bus that day. It was her goodbye. I looked out for her like I always did, but no, I never saw her again.'

While Jack had been talking, I'd put the camera down and sat next to him on the bench; it hadn't felt right to be taking his picture while he was telling me this precious story or to probe him with questions about the depth of his relationship with Sue. His eyes were misty and I wanted to take his hand; instead, I stroked Oscar.

'Anyhow,' he continued. 'Not long after that, us bus conductors were phased out in London. So I retrained to be a bus driver. It wasn't the same, no chatting with the passengers. And it was stressful, you know, to keep the bus on time. A couple of years ago, when I was on the night shift, a young guy got on at Roehampton, and he passed me without paying. *Lad! You forgot your fare*, I said. He turned round, in slow motion as it were, came back and punched me in the chest. That's what it felt like. A punch. I don't remember anything else. According to the passengers who witnessed it, he got out his knife, cool as you like, and stabbed me. Eighteen times. In the chest. He stabbed me while I was behind the wheel. Just like that. I'm still asking myself, why. I never had any bother when I was a conductor … never, not even with the scallywags. But there's no point asking why, is there? The guy had a bad day, that's all there is to say. I'm lucky. Because the doctors told me it was touch and go. I was in hospital for a few weeks. Got a scar,' he lifted his hand from Oscar to unbutton his shirt, and pulled down his T-shirt until I could see the bumpy white puckering of skin. 'I couldn't go back to work afterwards,' he said.

'What a terrible thing to happen to you, Jack,' I said, shocked and wondering to myself how anyone could maim this special soul. 'Is the scar still sore?'

'You won't believe it, but my broken heart hurt more. I laughed, though. Because you hear people say that they don't want to be a passenger in life, they want to be in the driving seat of their lives, don't you? … And when I hear them say it now, I tell them what happened to me … *Mate, when I was in the driving seat.*'

'You think you take control, but you can't predict what's going to happen – good, or bad.' I was stroking Oscar again; the breeze blew back the dog's fur, accentuating his delicate face.

'Yup. This one's the love of my life now. Aren't you, boy? Don't be deceived, though, he's a feisty little whatsit. Picks fights with dogs four times his size. Gets us into trouble. We were walking on the towpath down by Kew the other day, and he went for a Doberman … the owner started kicking Oscar and when I tried to pick him up he booted me and all, knocked me unconscious. These two nice ladies were passing. They called the police and ambulance. One of the ladies went with me to the hospital – they kept me in for the weekend and the other looked after Oscar until I came out. There are some good people around. That's why I'm moving to Brighton. I reckon it'll be better for us there. We'll be out of harm's way. And there's the sea, of course. Oscar likes the sea.'

Jack and I sat for a bit. He asked me about my life, and I wrote down his new Brighton address in my notebook and promised to post him his portrait, then we said goodbye and I continued with my walk, leaving them to absorb the hill and its view. Our encounter seemed otherworldly, and felt even more so at Hampstead Heath station much later that evening, when the carriage doors of the Overground train back to Richmond opened to reveal Jack and Oscar sitting there, facing me.

Recently, a client came into the jewellers where I work to ask whether we'd heard about *the stabbing*. We hadn't. She was jittery and apologetic about her appearance; *I don't think I've even brushed my hair*, she said. She lives a five-minute walk from the shop and had been woken at 4 a.m. by a commotion. From her bedroom window she saw a man staggering up the garden path. She ran downstairs and looked through the spyhole of the front door to see him there, bleeding profusely from the neck. He was crying, *Help! I'm dying*. She phoned for an ambulance. Our client's eyes were unnaturally wide as she was relaying this and she was clearly reliving the horror of what she saw, and I felt sorry for her witnessing such a thing. I said it must have been a comfort for him to have her by his side. She looked at me with even wider eyes. *I didn't open the door*, she said. *I had my teenage sons in the house. The perpetrator may have been there.* I was taken aback. That afternoon on Parliament Hill had suddenly flashed to mind, and all I could think of was how terrified the man on her doorstep must have been, and how freezing cold he must have felt. Over the next week or so, I asked friends and family, fifteen good, compassionate people, what they would have done if they'd found someone bleeding and begging for help on their front door. Only two of them would have opened the door to be with him. The others would have done what our client did, for the same or similar reasons, *better not give the emergency services additional victims; he might have stabbed someone himself and been injured in the ensuing struggle; he may have been dangerous, feigning the extent of his injury.* Evidently my response had been naive, given the current level of knife and gang crime in London. But in the spirit of Jack, and the two ladies on the Kew towpath, and of looking after people on their journeys, I still hope that I would have opened the door and done what I could to reassure and warm him.

Chapter Fifteen

'I know,' says Emily slowly, eyeing the bare 'four-poster' frame of my bed.

'What?'

'Patience, patience, Chickpea,' she's delving inside the bedside cabinet, 'now where've they gone ... ah! Here they are.' She's found the wad of get-well cards. 'Wow. What a collection,' she says leafing through them, some occasioning a raised eyebrow, a smile and a reread. It's not in Emily's make-up to sit still, she has to occupy every minute of each visit with meaningful action, whether it's massaging warmth into my ice-block feet, or smoothing out wrinkles in the surgical stockings, or brushing my hair, or sorting out my laundry. 'Let's get them up.' She pulls a chair over to the bed, stands on it, and hooks them over the frame, her paintbrush ponytail swinging with each card hung. We've often been mistaken for twins, which I've never understood because – apart from our hair and eyebrows – our features, though similar, are as different as our personalities. Her eyes are wider apart for a start, shaped like Daddy's. And she also inherited his practicality, for which I think he was heartily relieved; to have at least one daughter whose feet occasioned terra firma.

From the age of six, up to past my eighteenth birthday, we spent exactly half of every school holiday with him: when we were not occupied with the repair of some gate, rolling apples from the garden in newspaper for winter consumption, or the removal of rust from our bikes' mudguards – with a toothbrush

– or a marathon cycle ride, I would be curled into a book while Emily would be at his side in the kitchen as his sous-chef. *Come on Harriet, do go and help your father, you know how it'll please him,* Nom would say. It wasn't that I didn't want to help. My daydreaming and lack of dexterity frustrated him. He was impatient with my clumsiness and I, hating to be bad at anything, was sensitive to his raised voice. It wasn't the gently simmering pans on the hob that would catch fire.

'Springfield'
Wycliffe College
Lampeter
Cardiganshire
Wales
Great Britain
8th June, 1944

Dear Daddy,

I hope you are as well as I am. I have just returned from my first Scout camp. My job there was assistant cook – at least it was until I was elected chief cook. I must have inherited my talents from you and Mummy. If I remember rightly, you made a cake for a soldier in hospital in the last war and it was so good he would not believe it was all your own work. My duties as cook were never ending, but I received good praise from everyone ...

My father and I kitchen-synced over snacks, like sandwich making, where he plumped out two slices of bread or a pocket of pitta with combinations of flavour and imagination that would have impressed even Roald Dahl's Willy Wonka. I learnt to appreciate what became our picnic ritual as an art form, suddenly *mise en place* was exciting and I could peel and chop as finely as he required. In spring and summer the sandwiches would be packed up in panniers for twenty-mile bike hikes, or layered in Nom's wicker shopping basket that would be lodged between towels, kite and beach balls in the boot of my father's Citroen Dyane when we trundled off, roof rolled back, to Lyme Regis or Seaton ...

This old man. He played one. He played knick-knack on my drum. With a knick-knack paddywack give a dog a bone, this old man came rolling home. This old man. He played two. He played knick-knack on his shoe ... on we sing. *Who can see the sea?* Daddy asks. *I can, I can!* says five-year-old Emily, the sea nowhere yet in sight. Past patchwork fields. *Daddy, please may I have a wine gum?* I say. *Yes, and a black one for me, Sweetheart.* He hands over the scrunched white paper bag and Emily and I rummage. *Right, Harri. Tell us how a car engine works.* He'd explained it a few days ago. *Oh Christopher, how about a game of I-spy instead?* says Nom in the front with Sophie on her lap, the blond Pekingese's ears blowing in the wind. *No, go on, tell us Harriet,* he says, looking at me in the mirror. *Well it's this box. And inside the box there are pistons and things. And there are little people in there, like the slaves on a Roman galley ship and ...* Daddy lion laughs. *That's not quite the explanation I was anticipating,* he says and then, there, sparkling ahead, is a little strip of blue with dancing stars ... I see it! I see the sea!

There was a snack, though, that had star billing – that bonded us as close as he and Emily in the kitchen:

'Grab the biggest saucepan ... perfect, now cover the base with oil ... not too much. Whack up the heat and wait until it bubbles ...

there … look … yes, pour in the corn, just one layer. Good. Lid on. As soon as you hear the first pop, turn the gas right down.'

Pop. Pop. Pop. The saucepan lid jumps. Pop. Pop. Pop.

'Good … heat down. And look … now we shake it to blazes so none of the corn sticks to the saucepan.' And he's taken the pan with one hand on the lid and looks as if he's doing a jig the way he is hopping around. 'Can you still hear popping?' he says after a couple of minutes. There are just one or two lonely pops. 'Okay, it's stopped,' and he turns off the gas, removes the lid, and I sprinkle the hundreds of little clouds with a pinch of hickory salt and pepper.

We would tip the popcorn into one of Nom's china mixing bowls and then Emily and I cosied up either side of Daddy on the sofa, to watch David Attenborough's *Life on Earth*, or an old black-and-white film, our three hands colliding in the bowl. From the moment the flickering titles rolled and the dramatic soundtracks filled the room, I was captivated. Dramas, comedies, musicals, westerns, war films: I loved them all. It only added to my pleasure that he would explain in minute detail why various shots worked or didn't work, or how a certain effect had been achieved. I'm sure that most people would have found his interruptions infuriating, but I was intrigued.

Last night we had a film called *Hey Hey USA*. Will Hay was the hero and was he funny! I nearly laughed my head off. We have been having rain all week. I am getting quite good at billiards, I think the Americans call it pool.

Yesterday I saw *One Hundred Men and a Girl*. My has Deanna Durbin got a voice! When she first came on screen there were a lot of whistles but they soon died down.

There have been plenty of cards for Emily to cover all sides of the bed's four-poster frame. 'Like Christmas,' she says, casting a critical eye over her decorations. And as I admire her collage, I'm overwhelmed with love, and for the glimpses of our father that she evinces.

*

My mother continues to arrive on the dot of 2 p.m. each afternoon. Her business partner is shouldering the weight of their work while I'm here. They have a charity – **C**ookery **A**s **A L**ife **S**kill – that takes cookery back into the classroom; her special interest is in those schools that have children with special needs, whether it's Great Ormond Street Hospital School, Barnardo's, or schools where children are physically and mentally disadvantaged. After kissing me hello, the first thing she does is to see to the windows, to make sure some Hammersmith air is flowing into the room and, at my request, to pull down all the blinds – the brightness is still searing. Then she transfers the contents of her cool-bag to the minibar fridge and assembles me a small plate to tempt my appetite. I eat as much of it as I can, while she relays titbits of news. *Your mother always could tell a decent story, with accents – the lot, she used to make me howl with laughter,* Nom often told me with a teary eye, missing her daughter-in-law long after the divorce (and this was reflected by my own mother's wistful comments on my grandmother, *she was my best friend for quite a while*). She has the knack of framing a story, no matter how small, with the same care and colour she uses to wrap gifts, or to present these little plates of food. So, I'm momentarily lulled by her updates on Harvey and how he is ruling the roost with his dog-sitter; about a funny exchange she had at the supermarket. Afterwards she sits in the shuttered shade – *Are you sure you wouldn't like just a little* *more light in here? No? Okay* – and does the crossword as I try to doze in my chair.

It has been during my mother's and Emily's visits that I have snatched a snooze here and there, from out of the gargoyles' gaze. But that has stopped now. It is not only the white flash pain that is bothering me; since moving up here I have encountered a new phase of discomfort in my legs, arms and spine. At first I wondered whether my bed might have deflated again, until I remembered that I no longer had the waterbed. Mr Winkler is not sure what specifically is causing it and thinks another CT scan is in order. The Pain Team have been round, almost relieved that at long last I am complaining of hardcore pain and not the unresponsive nausea. *Could you describe the pain, Harriet?* The one with the clipboard flicks her hair; Miss Green is back. *In my bones. Deep.* I can barely move my lips, the hurt is so consuming. I visualise the murky glob that is systematically scraping away, hollowing out the insides of my bones like Pac-Man. *And, Harriet, on a scale of one to ten, how would you rate this pain?* Pen hovering over a box on the sheet she is completing. *Um. Nine.* The Fentanyl patches have been replaced with OxyNorm that I control through a pump on the reconnected IV every four hours. *It's a drug often given to cancer patients,* Miss Green said as if this would hearten me. Long gone are the occasions when I refused to use the pump. After the drug drips into my vein, there's about two hours of respite before bone ache returns to full throttle and my fingers start kneading, clawing the bedclothes, and I am given paracetamol. I cannot drag my eyes away from the hands of the wall clock for the remaining 120 minutes before I am able to press the pump again. Nothing shelters me, or my mother, from this the ache.

Days, then, are timetabled round OxyNorm. Jaw clamped, until 8 a.m. for the first dose, which just about covers the washing rigmarole. Second dose, 12 p.m., so that physio with Natasha can take place at 12.30 p.m. – before the Oxy, nurses had to turn her away – and then just about squeeze in lunch with my mother. Four p.m. for the third, and I can mull over some crossword clues and have something to eat at 5.30. When my mother leaves at around 7 p.m., I ask her to open all the blinds.

Much later I watch the night sky as if it were the screen of my personal cinema, pinpointing stars; following the flickering lights of planes in and out of Heathrow. Up here I am no longer spooked by the sound of Faith rattling down the corridor on her crutches. But the price for such peace is a swelling isolation: there is no ward life to distract me when I am alone, no Mr Mohammed and Elsa for company. This gargoyle sidles up next to me in these early hours with chilling thoughts spilling from his eyes:

'It feels like ants crawling all over my face,' he says, flicking at his cheeks and nose.

'Careful of the dressing, Daddy.' I take his hand and guide it back to rest on his chest. I leave my hand – warm over his – for a moment, noting our identically turned-in right forefingers. He is lying down, I am sitting cross-legged, my knees touching him, on his bed, on the very same textured counterpane where I remember Emily being placed, on my parents' bed, a day old. That was in Somerset, but this is twenty years later in Cardiff. *It sounds so grand, 33A, Rawden Place*, he laughed when he first moved in, about five years ago. He loved that the house lay snug in the city's least gentrified area of Riverside. That the corner shop stocked heavyweight sacks of rice and spices, pistachios, cashews, peanuts. *What a termite I've become,* he said, patting his stomach. That it was walking distance from the old Pontcanna television studios where he could go and meet his chums for a *few* pints to chew over old times. From the front, No. 33A looked like a miniature townhouse, but inside it was a Tardis, stretching back and back, and even had a self-contained flat where Emily and I would sleep. He rented the flat out once, to Crazy Jane. One Friday evening she invited him up to join a dinner party, fish was on the menu. The next day he stood in the courtyard staring at his pond in disbelief: two of his beloved giant carp were missing. My father never rented it out again.

'Harriet.' He'd phoned me a few weeks ago. 'It's back. The cancer.'

'Oh, Daddy. No. Where?' After his last drunken outburst at Nom's I had decided not to speak to him. Until he apologised. *For all I care, you can fuck off to the moon and not come back.* He'd had no recollection of his words the next day, but by then they were spray-painted red over the walls of my mind. This development, though, kind of bleached them out. *Please don't let him die.*

'In my sinus again. They want to operate. Soon. I'll be in for a couple of days.' His voice is fathoms low. 'Apparently I'll need someone to collect me from the hospital. And to be in the house for a bit afterwards. Will you ...?'

'Yes, yes, of course, Daddy.'

'I don't want anyone else there.'

'What about Nom?'

'No. I might not even tell her. I don't want her worrying. I don't want any fuss.'

I got the call to pick him up from University Hospital a few days after the surgery. He had been adamant that I shouldn't visit during his stay. A nurse escorted him down to the entrance. His left eye looked askew, as if it had slipped slightly down his face; the white was crisscrossed with a network of bloody rivers and gauze covered much of his nose and nostrils. The nurse handed me his overnight bag and some boxes of medication. *You'll have to put in the eye drops,* she said before shaking my father's hand, *pop by and see us when you come back for your radiotherapy, Mr Mercer.*

'Looks like your old dad has been in a few rounds with Muhammad Ali, doesn't it?' he said after she had gone.

'Since when have I ever been allowed to call you *Dad*?' I asked, finding his hand. 'Anyway, you're not old!' He was fifty-seven and I suppose, numbers-wise, he'd been old compared to my friends' dads, but he'd more than matched them in energy and spirit.

We had walked the short distance to my Morris Minor. 'You know,' he said, patting his pockets as I opened the passenger door, 'I felt very amorous towards the nurse when I came round in recovery. When I opened my eyes and saw her face, she was, believe me, for that moment, the most desirable woman in the world.'

'Daddy, what are you doing? She said not to bend.' I was half laughing, not sure whether I was more perplexed at hearing my father talking in this way or by his attempt to look in his overnight bag.

'Trying to find some change for your parking, I've got some somewhere.'

'No, no, please just get in the car.'

He goes to move his hand again, but then remembers and leaves it on his chest. I stroke his brow, smoothing the ants away.

'That's nice,' he says.

'Are you in any other pain?'

'It's okay. Tell you what, though; it was eye-watering when they removed the packing. Excruciating.'

'Packing?'

'Some kind of webbing that they'd stuck up my nose during surgery. It took them over an hour to pull it out.'

I had stayed with him for a couple of weeks; in the first few days his room became our cocoon. He slept a lot, and when he woke I'd make him something to eat, put in his eye drops, check his dressing, and then we would watch a film or chat until he fell asleep again. He was so stoical. I unclench my fists from the sheets. And take some deep breaths to try and blow away the bone ache. My thoughts circle the third time his cancer returned. Twelve years later. This time he cut himself off from the world: from Emily and me, his sisters and my mother, with whom he had eventually retained a friendship of sorts, and the hospital. The boat he always said he was going to sail. How he suffered. *Look, all cancer is vicious, but cancer of the sinus is particularly pernicious. Relatively rare, though … it's often contracted by carpenters … something to do with wood dust …* my GP told me reluctantly, when I pushed him for information. My father bled to death. After months alone. I cannot get his pain out of my head. I see him lying there on his bed, on that same bedspread. Scared. No one to soothe his brow. To bring him sustenance. To tell him they loved him.

Chapter Sixteen

REKOJ
JOKER

The comic, the entertainer, the jester, savours the reflection of his smile in his viewers' faces; for a moment one can imagine he believes what he sees.[53]

During his Oscar-winning portrayal of Arthur Fleck in *Joker*, Joaquin Phoenix has to laugh – a lot. Since childhood, Fleck has been told by his mother that his *purpose in life is to bring laughter and joy into this cold, dark world*; to this end he is an aspiring stand-up comedian, and works – until he's sacked – as a clown at Ha-Ha's hire-a-clown agency. He also lives with mental illness – his mother's, and his own. It was odd to leave the cinema after Phoenix's arresting performance with laughter ringing in my ears. But which laugh? Because Fleck has three laughs: was it the fake one, for when he's trying to fit in with the more usual behaviour of others; or was it the episodic uncontrollable laughter that chokes Fleck when he's particularly stressed and which he explains with a laminated card, *Forgive my laughter I have a condition?*[54] Or was it the antihero's least used laugh, his genuine one, heard at the

---

53   David Grossman, *A Horse Walks into a Bar*. Translated by Jessica Cohen (Great Britain: Jonathan Cape, 2016), p.18

54   The condition isn't named as such, although we know it results from a brain injury and is reminiscent of Pseudobulbar affect.

end of the film. I think it was his fake laughter that accompanied me back to the car as I began to digest *Joker*. The laughter in general, though, brought my father to mind. Not because my father was a sociopath (as Fleck becomes), but because he had a very distinctive and loud laugh. It was, as my grandmother said, a guffaw; there was nothing shrill or forced about it, but its visceral resonance could indeed be shocking.

Much would make my father laugh. He had a tremendous eye for life's incongruities, and the absurd; the way he evoked the smallest detail of an anecdote could turn it into a hilarious sketch. His puns would have given Milton Jones a run for his money; limericks rolled off his tongue; and *HLS!* was his familiar, gleeful cry when my sister and I fell for his pranks hook, line and sinker. He drip-fed us comedy: Laurel and Hardy, Spike Milligan, *The Two Ronnies*, Carla Lane, Kenny Everett, Victoria Wood, Monty Python, *Cheers* and Joan Rivers. Humour was integral to his living. When he threw back his head and let rip, I couldn't help joining in, his laughter was contagious. And confusing. For as often as he guffawed, he would be consumed by periods of blackness, and there were occasions when I popped my head round his bedroom door in the middle of the day, to discover him curled up on his bed, locked in a foetal position, unresponsive to my 'Daddy?'

It was difficult to reconcile his sense of humour with his depression. I diagnose depression in retrospect because male mental health was not even whispered about back then; he might very occasionally admit to feeling low, but never depressed. He self-anaesthetised with alcohol. His family – with the exception of my grandmother – had little empathy for his condition. They lost respect and patience. He became an embarrassment to them, and was dismissed as difficult, and a drinker. It's true: my father hadn't helped himself by wielding his katana tongue at family gatherings, and generally allowing alcohol to take command.

He'd metamorphose from charm itself to this seething demon in the time it took for his eyes to become bloodshot. But everyone seemed only too eager to judge, rather than to seek to understand. And yet for all the complexity of their six-year marriage, my mother has only ever spoken kindly of my father. It was her suggestion to ask his friend and erstwhile colleague, Terry, to give the eulogy at his funeral.

... Chris was greatly talented, gifted and creative ... The Number One TV director and producer of the time, responsible for trailblazer of all pop music shows with *Discs A Go Go*. Then there was his award winning *Land of Song*: it was a great responsibility for Chris, an Englishman, to project an image of Wales into millions of homes throughout the UK ... He was professionally a very generous man. In my early career he invited me to co-produce and direct *Discs A Go Go* ... it was live TV where mistakes could not be re-recorded ... no one who could have taught me more ... it was learning by osmosis. He was by no means perfect, whilst he had The Rolling Stones on the show, he turned down The Beatles! He was a taskmaster, had the knack of reducing people to tears, it was nothing personal ... he was a perfectionist ... he would insist on pushing everyone to their limits. Himself most of all. He even pushed technology. He would not stand back uninvolved ... He was incredibly knowledgeable and we would discuss everything from quantum physics to life after death.

These were compassionate words; the two men hadn't seen each other since Terry had been at the receiving end of one of my father's alcohol-fuelled tirades, but he understood that alcohol had been a mask. While I've found it hard to make sense of my father's drinking, and been angry, I've always been aware that it was symptomatic of some soul-fracturing fissure, and knew that – underneath everything – he possessed exceptional perception, colossal gentleness, and humour.

My father, then, was as much a funny person as he was sad, and I'm reminded of the starkness of this dichotomy whenever I hear media discussions of why it is a large proportion of comedians endure depression. When Arthur Fleck researches stand-up routines, he goes to a comedy club to watch Gary Gulman; it's surely no coincidence that Gulman was selected for this cameo role, having made *The Great Depresh*[55] based on his real-life experience of depression. Mike Bernstein's US documentary *Laughing Matters* (released on World Mental Health Awareness Day, 2019) opens with news footage of comedians (including John Belushi and Robin Williams) who died from unnatural causes and discusses, through the personal stories of eleven young current comedians, how depression and anxiety affect their profession. It asks why it is that some of the funniest people are the saddest. Sarah Silverman maintains that 'all of us learn a skillset inherently as children that gets us through childhood. 100% of comedians became comedians because somewhere in their childhood they needed to be funny in order to survive …' It's a theory evidently shared by David Grossman when he textured his stand-up comedian protagonist, Dovaleh G, for his novel that went on to win the Man Booker International Prize 2017, *A Horse Walks into a Bar*,[56] and that came to mind while I was watching *Joker*.

The reader joins narrator Avishai Lazar, a retired Supreme Court Judge, and his fellow audience members (a disparate crowd including soldiers, bikers and a medium), at a small comedy

55 *The Great Depresh*, (HBO, 2019)

56 David Grossman, *A Horse Walks into a Bar*. Translated by Jessica Cohen (Great Britain: Jonathan Cape, 2016)

club in Netanya, Northern Israel, for an evening of hilarity with
Dovaleh G on his fifty-seventh birthday (*It's not easy getting to fifty-
seven, and that's after surviving the Holocaust and the Bible ...*).[57]
We learn that Avishai and Dovaleh were friends that last saw each
other as teenagers at Gadna Camp; that Dovaleh invited him out
of the blue to critique his final performance as a stand-up comic.
The judge is grieving for the passing of his wife and, in any event,
is not a fan of stand-up comedy, but acquiesces – haunted by the
memory of witnessing Dovaleh thrown around in a duffel bag by
bullies at Gadna Camp, and not having intervened. The novel lasts
for the duration of Dovaleh's routine, which we watch through
Avishai's eyes (and through our fingers); it is without chapters,
and in spite of Dovaleh's own laughs, the audience's laughs are
few and far between. His jokes mostly target Israel's conflict with
Palestine, and women, and their derogatory nature corresponds
with emphasis of his unattractive smile; it's *a clownish gaping grin;
a skeleton-smile*; his face *stretches into a toxic jeer; a mocking grin;*
he gives a heckler *an ill-conceived man-to-man grin that makes
him look away as though he'd seen an open wound*; and it reminds
Avishai of *a little rodent gnawing on himself*. Jokes, however, are
not the mainstay of his routine. Unbeknownst to the audience,
Dovaleh is in Netanya not to make them laugh per se but to share
the punchlines of *the wild and hilarious story* of his first funeral
... *Hands together for death!,* the delivery of which leaves them
bewildered and frustrated. Throughout the routine he raises
their expectations by exuding all the panache and rhythm of an
elite comedian; his energy is high as he variously *dances, prances,
tap-dances, skips, darts, zig-zags,* and *dashes* across the stage: he
should be funny, and his audience should be in fits of laughter, but
Dovaleh's stories leave them crumpling in *opaque distress*.

---

57   Grossman, *A Horse Walks into a Bar*, p.50

A few minutes into his routine, the underlying tone of the show is established:

> He lifts his shirt up again, this time rolling it slowly, seductively, exposing us to a sunken belly with a horizontal scar, a narrow chest and frighteningly prominent ribs, the taut skin shriveled and dotted with ulcers.[58]

The scar, lesions and Dovaleh's cancer-ridden, emaciated body are metaphors for the emotional traumas that began in childhood. Similarly, fifteen minutes into *Joker*, we watch Fleck at work, getting dressed for a day of clowning. He's sitting on a bench, bent over, in front of some lockers. The camera pans to his bruised, naked upper torso. He's shockingly skeletal: his spine juts, and every muscle ripples with exertion as he stretches his clown shoes: it's a powerful scene. Both protagonists' physiques are clear signifiers of their mental health: Grossman and Todd Phillips[59] want our sympathy early on in order for us to empathise, even if in part, with their *treacherous* jokers (obviously aware that for many it's more difficult to empathise with the bleeding, invisible wound of the mind, than with a sutured, bandaged limb).

Dovaleh's 'first funeral story' is built on Jewish history, its effect on his mother, and how it in turn impacted his growing up. His parents were immigrants to Israel, and his mother's escape from a concentration camp left her *the most unhinged thing in the world, and the saddest;*[60] *She could walk around all day long with*

---

58 Grossman, *A Horse Walks into a Bar*, p.8

59 Todd Phillips, Director and Co-writer of *Joker*

60 Grossman, *A Horse Walks into a Bar*, p.10

her face on the ground and the schmatte on her head;[61] *she wore boots come rain or shine having walked 30 miles in snow barefoot.*[62] He reflects on how his clowning began in childhood, *I spent my whole life trying to make her laugh;*[63] he succeeds in making her laugh with his failed attempts at walking on his hands. And then, when he eventually masters the art of handwalking, he finds his own refuge;

> I got calm, I got happy. All I could hear was the blood in my ears, and then quiet, all the noise stopped, and I finally felt like I'd found one place in the air of the world where there was no one except me.[64]

He handwalked from room to room at home despite his father's beatings, he went to school on his hands uncaring that it encouraged his bullies. It shields him in crisis: when news is broken at Gadna Camp that he needs to leave immediately to attend a family funeral the same afternoon – although not told which family member – it dawns on the adolescent Dovaleh that one of his parents has died, and he instinctively flips upside down and handwalks to the truck waiting to transport him to the Jerusalem crematorium; he doesn't care that the sand's *hot as hell* and scorches his palms because *who's gonna find me when I'm upside down?* And at the funeral, after discovering it's his mother who has passed away, he cannot bear to look at his violent father, or contemplate being hugged by him.

---

61 Grossman, *A Horse Walks into a Bar,* p.78

62 Grossman, *A Horse Walks into a Bar,* p.110

63 Grossman, *A Horse Walks into a Bar,* p.75

64 Grossman, *A Horse Walks into a Bar,* p.76

I'll kill him ... And the second I had that thought, my body flipped me upside down. Flung me up, threw me on my hands, the yarmulke fell off and I heard everyone breathing and it went quiet.[65]

And he escapes the crematorium, using his 'skillset'.

As Arthur Fleck makes notes on Gulman's performance and attire, he fake laughs his approval; when he returns to the club for his first attempt at open mic, he finds himself on stage overwhelmed by uncontrollable laughter, gagging and clutching at his throat, unable to breathe. And within the claustrophobic walls of the Netanya comedy club when Dovaleh attempts to demonstrate his handwalking to his audience, his legs no longer have the strength and he falls flat on the face of his current mental state; *These days I can barely make it on my feet.*[66] He lacks motivation to get out of bed, let alone to do stand-up. Dovaleh's life-story driven routine suggests Freudian relief, where the stand-up stage and mic enables comedians space to relieve themselves of demons – however depressed they feel off-stage. But the deeper into his routine Dovaleh dances, the more tortured his delivery becomes, and the more self-harming he becomes. At the beginning of the routine he slaps himself in emphasis *leaving a white splotch on his forehead turning red;*[67] towards the routine's climax, Avishai watches Dovaleh become so frustrated by his audience that he attacks them – by beating himself up:

The fist flies so fast that I hardly see it. I hear the click of teeth hitting each other, and his whole face seems wrenched away

---

65 Grossman, *A Horse Walks into a Bar*, p.193

66 Grossman, *A Horse Walks into a Bar*, p.47

67 Grossman, *A Horse Walks into a Bar*, p.12

from his neck in an instant. His glasses fall to the floor. He doesn't alter his expression. Just breathes heavily in pain. With two fingers he props up the corner of his mouth: Still not funny? Not at all? ... He slaps his face, ribs, stomach.[68]

In the opening minute of *Joker*, Arthur Fleck is painting on his clown make-up; when he's finished reddening his lips he gazes into the mirror, and like Dovaleh *props up the corner of his mouth* with two fingers into a gum-whitening and grotesque smile while tears drip down from his Pierrot eyes, smudging the make-up. When Dovaleh beats himself:

> The spectacle looks like a fight between at least two men ... Two threads of blood dribble down from his nostrils to his mouth ...[69]

For anyone with depression, and particularly for those comedians for whom depression and humour coexist in such polarity, it must indeed feel, on some days, as if their mind is a boxing ring for their brutal selves. I'm sure it did for my father. Although there is no conclusive evidence to suggest that comedians suffer from depression more than anyone else, it's intriguing that David Grossman should conjure both a comedian who is happiest when he's upside down, and the conceit of comedy club as painful place, having himself been on close terms with grief and trauma.[70]

---

68   Grossman, *A Horse Walks into a Bar*, p.152

69   Grossman, *A Horse Walks into a Bar*, p153

70   David Grossman's twenty-year-old son died in the last hours of the second Lebanon War in 2006. His grief nuanced his final draft of *To the End of the Land* (2008); and his extraordinary play-poem, *Falling Out of Time* (2014), is about a couple coming to terms with the loss of their son.

When I was about seven or eight, my father designed and made me a red and white clown's outfit, complete with Pierrot hat. It was so detailed and made from crepe paper. He sewed the pieces together meticulously and I wore it that afternoon with white tights and full make-up – actually not that dissimilar from Arthur Fleck's.

... I still hear my father guffaw. Mostly at the cinema. Or theatre. His laughter roars from my belly and out of my mouth faster than Shelly-Ann Fraser-Price off her 100m blocks, and before those around me have even broken into a smile, let alone discreetly chuckled. Ironically, the film that's probably earned me the most elbow-nudges of all time was Maren Ade's *Toni Erdmann* (2016), there was much in the character of the prankster Winfried that reminded me of my father, down to his fake teeth, and the father–daughter relationship was reminiscent of ours; it had me guffawing and sobbing in equal measures.

Chapter Seventeen

'Right, holding on to the Zimmer, rise up on your tiptoes ... perfect ... and now back down again ... slowly,' instructs Natasha, 'this'll help with balance.' In spite of the dragging weight of my stomach, I like the exercise. It feels as if I am limbering up for an Olympic challenge. The *Chariots of Fire* soundtrack recedes, however, when I look down and remember that instead of vest, track shorts and running spikes, I'm wearing an outsized sweatshirt over my T-shirt nightie, the long white surgical stockings and sheepskin slippers. 'Straighten up, head up ... good.' She gets me to repeat it ten times or so. 'You could maybe do this two or three times a day.' As soon as each subsequent dose of OxyNorm kicks in, I'm up on my tiptoes. On his next visit, I show Mr Winkler my new party trick. Perhaps it is my gritted, manic grin – the tiara to my outfit – that causes the raised eyebrows. *Great, Harriet. Just don't overdo it*, he says.

The physio progress, though, is slow. Before this happened I was walking over thirty miles a week, and now the Zimmer and I have yet to make the bathroom. When I look at the distance from the chair or bed, I wonder how it can be that a few normal strides can span into infinity. *I'm still a figurine in Slinkachu land, drunk from Alice in Wonderland's draught. That's what it must be.* My visitors are ballet dancers: they move with lightness, effortless ease. They don't think twice about getting up from their chairs and gliding over to the windows to remark upon the sun glinting on the Thames. I yearn for my favourite green spaces that I roam with Harvey. I crave the green of walks, of hills that disappear into the horizon. I want to drink litres of green. I want to roll in green, inhale it until every thought is saturated with the life, and movement, that it represents. But then Bone-Ache wrinkles back its lips and laughs hysterically – baring its stained hyena teeth – at images of me walking in Bushy Park again.

One morning when I buzz for a bedpan, I wait some time until a nurse who I haven't seen before answers my call.

'I hear you've been having a bit of a rough time. I'm Sarah, and I'm going to make sure you have a *lovely* day today,' she breezes.

'Now why don't we try a commode, it's *much* more comfortable.' She smiles knowledgeably. 'It's kind of urgent ... maybe next time?' I say, but Sarah has already disappeared out of the door. If I could cross my legs, they would now be crossed. I hear her chat with someone in the corridor; a few minutes pass. And a few more. She reappears pushing a chair on wheels that she parks close to my chair, and with a theatrical flourish removes the disguised seat, 'Ta dah!' she says, as if revealing a wall safe. It's another thirty minutes of negotiating the white flashing pain before I am settled on this throne, fit to burst.

'Right then. You buzz when you're done and I'll be right back,' Sarah beams, this time closing the door behind her.

It *is* more comfortable. My bladder gushes with gratitude. Something is very wrong. It sounds like a waterfall rather than a stream contained in a pan. Mid-pee, unable to stop, my heart sinks and my suspicions are confirmed, and my humiliation complete, when I notice the gradually expanding dark circle on the blue carpet. I buzz. It is a long five minutes before Sarah bustles back to find my flooded mortification.

'Oh silly me, I forgot to check whether the pot was secure. Never mind, I'm sure this carpet's seen worse. You mustn't think it's *your* fault,' she sing-songs.

Back in the chair, I feel helpless and ridiculous as I watch her mop up.

'There, you can barely notice it,' she says, hand on hip, gesturing at the stain.

'Now, I'm going to make your bed *beautifully*. Nothing like lovely clean sheets, is there?' More beatific smiles and a mound of bedding piles next to the lagoon patch, before it is crisply reassembled, complete with hospital corners. The whirlwind that is Nurse Sarah leaves, promising to look in on me shortly. I am exhausted.

I want to share this episode with Emily ... my mobile is not on the bedside cabinet, and is nowhere to be seen from my chair.

I buzz. A different nurse arrives. She searches high and low: on the table, under the bed, behind the bed, in the bedside cabinet, under and through my mother's collection of crossword-filled newspapers, but to no avail. She fetches Sarah.

'Harry Potter and the case of the missing phone, is it? Let's just see if it got caught up in the bedding, shall we?' Sarah beams as she unmakes my bed. No sign of it, and she looks in all the places the other nurse has just checked. We retrace my phone's movements: my mother had called shortly before I buzzed for the bedpan, and no one else had been in the room.

'I tell you what Harriet, I'm going to have a wee chat with Laundry just to see if they've found it amongst the sheets.' A frown creases Nurse Sarah's brow. Later the ward sister comes in. 'I'm afraid Laundry haven't found it yet ... but I think it's only a matter of time. I've called your number and it goes straight to answerphone. It must be getting a jolly good soap,' she says, remaking the bed. There's a mass of paperwork registering the loss. It's only a phone but I'm sad to have lost the texts from friends that I like to reread during the night. I don't see Nurse Sarah again.

*

It's gone 7 p.m., my mother has just left for the evening, but I hear determined footsteps approach. An explosion of Puffa jacket, tousled hair and amber eyes enter the room.

'Harri Heart!' Tania's at my bedside in two strides. I'm blinking again, at this unexpected and sun-bright sight of my best friend. 'You don't look half as bad as I'd thought you'd look,' she says bending to kiss my cheek, her perfume knocking me out with familiarity. 'I thought there'd be loads of tubes and wires.'

'Have no idea how I look,' I say. 'Nice to see you.'

'Well, you look as if you've been in the wars, but nothing how I'd imagined and still your lovely Harri Heart self,' she says stroking my hair. 'Emily's message … what a shock.'

'I didn't know she called you.'

'I got back from Almeria, and there were about five messages. I was scared to phone her back.' She takes off her coat, sits in a chair way off from my bed and delves into her bag, bringing out a four-pack of Guinness.

'Want one? Go on, I dare you.' She cracks open a can.

'You'll be rolling up next,' I say.

'What? Do the windows open?'

'Don't make me laugh. It hurts.'

'Seriously … just a teensy sip?' I shake my head and she swigs back from the opened can. 'Harri Heart, I'm sorry I haven't visited before.'

'I haven't wanted visitors.'

'Yes. I know. But I should've come earlier … you understand why I didn't, don't you? My father … those memories … of him in hospital. I didn't want to lose you too. Such a coward, sorry … you won't be able to get rid of me now.'

'I'm sorry for … for …' I want to apologise for making her relive those memories, but I can't find the verb. Tania doesn't seem to notice, she chats on and I luxuriate in the warmth of her company.

'The cards look so pretty up there,' she says, pointing up to them when she leaves an hour or so later.

Their designs face outward, but during the night I look up and trace squiggles and loops of handwriting, and snatches of messages float down and settle as delicately as cherry blossom on my thoughts:

… I know that this is the beginning of good and lovely things, with a little patience … I hope you feel more yourself shortly … So uncomplaining over something which must be horribly lonely and scary … Rest well, get well and be well … For years I have looked a gauche, a droit, a gauche, a droit, tout droit and not found anyone with your sensitivity, strength, warmth, joy and humour … I saw a rainbow on Tuesday, 11th March … Emily mentioned that your sparkle and humour are still very much present, good to hear … So pleased you are on the 'up' … What's black and white, and black and white? A penguin rolling down the hill … I'm thinking of you and hoping you are feeling better soon … Nothing I can say is adequate, or may sound trite and irrelevant … You will soon be better and giving me grief … Hopefully you'll be feeling stronger everyday … I did not get you a traditional 'Get Well' card - I thought you would prefer this, reminds me of you going round my garden last summer, photographing the flowers … Hope you are soon looking forward to going home

... You are a fighter ... Get well soon, missing you already ... You're in my thoughts and prayers ... Hope you're soon feeling completely well again ... For our precious sweetheart, Harriet ... Feel better soon (we need that Korean meal) ... Lots of little prayers have been whispered ... Hurry up and come home, it's too quiet on Fridays ... We are so pleased that you are making lots of small progress steps - each step is in the right direction ... What a scare you gave us ... I hope you are comfortable and recovering well ... Dear Hat, I love the way that u treated my teddy love Maddy ... Bushy Park is waiting for you ... Get well soon ... I cannot wait to discuss *The Kite Runner* with you ...

The faces of my well-wishers appear in front of me like benevolent ghosts. Heady and hazy, I visualise a green, green wide-open space and a picnic. Family, friends. There is laughter. My father's guffaw is the loudest. I search for him among all the faces but it's just the colour of his sound that I see. Alice and Maddy are running barefoot through dewy, jewelled grass. They can run forever, feather light. And they do. Through endless fields. I don't know how I can keep up. It's as if I'm on stilts, with the breeze in my hair. On they hurtle, not pausing until they reach Monet's bridge, they do-si-do across the wooden slats (I see flowering lily pads in their cheeks) straight into the Honeychurches' garden at Windy Corner. Gate-crashing. Now I'm alone. The garden has changed. Not manicured, practically wild. I hover, lightheaded from the all-pervading scents, my eyes dining on verdancy. *What wondrous life is this I lead!* It's so beautifully warm *Ripe apples drop about my head* and I am trapped in a verse *The luscious clusters of the vine Upon my mouth do crush their wine,* printed words lie at my feet. As I pick them up and try to read them *The nectarine and curious peach Into my hands themselves do reach*, they are snatched back by the ivy-winding undergrowth *Stumbling on melons as I pass, Insnared with flowers, I fall on grass.*[71] I'm in a leafy passage, it's still deliciously warm, the nectarine bursts on my lips, a golden light filters through the woven greens – I luxuriate in the moment, drenched in peace; the next breath, I am nauseated and claustrophobic, scrambling, desperate to get out of the greenness that is knitting out the light. The end is nothing but a trompe l'oeil. *Open your eyes. You're not even asleep*, I remind my panicking self; my eyelids are jammed shut and the passage becomes grainy like sand, dissolving into a crumbling red-brick wall.

*

'Let's take it again.' The nurse smiles and pulls open a second disposable thermometer. Before I can ask why, she pops it under my tongue and we wait another minute as she scans my recent sets of obs.

'No, you're definitely cooking up,' she says, looking at the dotted strip, '38 … how are you feeling?' She's looking concerned.

'Fine,' I say, nausea drumming my tummy as I remember Mr Winkler's threat of being returned back downstairs at 37.5. 'Really fine.' I try to saturate my tone with as much surprise and indignation as I can summon. While I'm still in the considerable clutches of Bone-Ache, I don't feel any different from how I've been feeling for the past five or so days.

'I think I'd better let the doctors know.'

'Oh no, please don't.'

---

71 Excerpts from *The Garden*, by Andrew Marvell

'It's just that it says on your notes …'

'Not yet.'

'Okay, you've just had your paracetamol, so let's see if it helps,' she concedes.

I spend the rest of the day crunching ice cubes as my obs have been increased from every three hours to hourly. At Rookesbury I ran myself an almost scalding bath and presented my heat rash as the German Measles that was doing the rounds. It got me out of four or five days of classes. *How could I have wasted time like that?* The iced ruse is successful and the fever obediently returns to normal.

*

The room is full: my mother, Simon, Emily, Tania and about seven nurses have their noses against the rain-splashed windows. It's the Boat Race, and they're watching Oxford and Cambridge slog it out under Hammersmith Bridge in choppy conditions. I sit in my chair, layered in blankets; a spectator of their excitement as they shriek and laugh their running commentary, a time lapse of that emanating from the BBC on the overhead television. … *a ropey old day for the oarsmen … it's nip and tuck at the moment … a real ding-dong battle here … Oxford under pressure, the light blues are really in it now … a gruelling exercise in steely harmony …* Bone-Ache chews away, as contentedly as a dog with its bone in front of a blazing log fire; I fight with myself not to feel despondent that I have neither the desire nor strength to be standing there with them. *Ah it's not so bad, Harriet,* I tell myself. *You could be paralysed. You're fortunate. You are going to recover.* All the same, I'm filled with a sanctimonious desire – I want my visitors to know that they should never take their body for granted, that none of us is invincible.

*

There's a short little knock. A nurse, maybe.

The door swings open.

'Alright, Toots?'

There, sitting in a wheelchair, in his camel dressing gown, is my distinguished looking friend and his son.

'Mr Mohammed,' I say. His face splits into the same smile that lit my way out of those cavernous moments on the observation ward.

'Look at the size of this room! There's quite enough room for Elsa and myself to join you!'

'Yes! Didn't you both get the invite?'

'Nice to see you, Harriet. Back in half an hour or so,' says the son, laughing, having positioned his father's chair next to mine.

'How are you, Mr Mohammed?'

'To be frank, Toots, I'm getting frustrated now. Still waiting for the blood pressure to go down before they allow me home,' he sighs. 'I was going to say it's been quiet without you.' His eyes sparkle with unexpected mischief.

'How's Elsa?' I say, giggling.

'She sends her good wishes. She's going to phone you. Word has it she'll be discharged tomorrow. And then I'll be without both my wingmen ... what to do. Pray. That's all ...'

'Mrs Mohammed?'

'Ah. My dear wife. She's become most worryingly strict with my snacks, as it happens. What about you, Toots? How are you?'

'On the mend. Like you, want to be home.'

'Be patient for a little longer. It'll make your return all the sweeter ... if only I could listen to my own advice,' he smiles at me. 'How's your marvellous mother, still here every day?'

'Yup, every day. She is marvellous. I don't know where I would've been without her, or my sister.'

He asks about the food up here, tells me about one of the nurses who's broken his wrist, and then we sit in companionable tranquillity. This is how my mother finds us, side by side with blankets over our knees like two elderly friends sitting on a bench, admiring the sea view on a cold, sunny winter's day.

*

I jump. Who is that?

My exercises are paying off and – no doubt propelled by the commode catastrophe – I have become nimbler with the Zimmer: I am surveying the bathroom for the first time. A feral creature hunches before me. The length of her neck looks jaundiced, marbled yellow. I look closer and see that it is bruising. Staring out from curtains of long, darkly stringy hair are grey eyes – wildly huge for her face – flecked with shards and shards of glittery fear. Her collarbones jut white and fleshless. My heart is hammering, as if a hooded figure has bundled me into the back of a van.

'Harriet? Are you okay?' Natasha says from the bathroom doorway.

'Harriet?' I watch her touch the creature's elbow. Gently. Natasha's golden face smiles.

'I've been kidnapped,' I say. And I play back Anders's, Susan's and Tania's words: *I expected you to look much worse.* It's the creature's eyes that disturb me the most. They are not mine. I think of the times I've returned the gargoyles' gaze, while they sucked.

I turn the Zimmer away from the mirror and look out of the window, and down onto rows of rooftops, lid upon lid to terraced houses; I can make out a parade of shops and see an ant person emerge from a grocer's. It is as if I'm watching life in the remotest region of the world – where I do not belong. I'm not sure whether I've overstretched my physical capabilities or whether it is viewing people going about their everyday lives that is so dizzying.

Chapter Eighteen

Memories from a knocked-down world

On my desk, and next to John's photograph, is a piece of ginger. A remnant, to be precise. We bought it from the Asian supermarket along with enoki mushrooms and bok choy for a soup recipe we'd spotted in the paper. Back then the ginger was especially fragrant and juicy to the slice. Now, eighteen months later, it has shrivelled to a quarter of its size and weight; it looks like dried porcini, and when I bring it to my nose, its scent is faintly sour. I took it from John's kitchen a few days after we made the soup, and the day after he died. John had been a member of the book club I ran for two years before we began seeing one another in January 2017. An erudite reader – who also possessed huge warmth and humour – I relished his choice of books and valued his eye for detail. I had invited him for a bite to eat, to thank him for editing my writing. True to form, he identified 92 typos in the draft; 89 with which I agreed. It had been a risk, for he might have loathed my writing; and it struck me, on the first book club meeting after receiving his notes, that I may as well have been sitting naked in front of him – he had read stuff about me that not even my family knew. *I did wonder about that*, he said, in his soft Lancashire voice, as we sipped gin. And so it began there, on that date that wasn't a date, at that relatively unimaginative choice of pub.

*

We went for long, long walks in Bushy Park. I was always admiring of John's lightness of step and fitness on these rambles; *You could've been a dancer*, I said as he jetéd over a puddle. It was a shock, then, when in March he began suffering headaches, and developed a gait that made him look as if he was crossing the deck of a boat tossed by stormy waves. A tumour, snug in his cerebellum, was diagnosed. It seemed natural that I should accompany him on every hospital trip, the planned and the unplanned; *You didn't sign up for this*, he said on one of them. He was superhumanly brave, determined that we should continue with all we had been enjoying. On the morning that John was due to see the neurosurgeon (the first consultation since the diagnosis six weeks previously), he didn't respond to my calls or texts. I went round to his flat; there was no answer, and so I called 999. The police broke in. Through the letterbox, we had heard his voice, thin and mumbling. In the split second that I stepped over the threshold of his bedroom, I knew the scene would be with me for life, and I know John would want me to keep the details to myself. What was important was that I took his head in my lap, and his hand in my hand. I did my best to reassure him. Later, at hospital, he lost consciousness and was put on a life-support machine. The following morning, they turned the machine off with his beloved family, and me, at his bedside, playing his favourite Bowie tracks. It was a five-month relationship that held a lifetime of intensity.

John died in May, and it seemed that wherever I stepped, happiness and carefreeness popped up around me like daisies opening to the warm, sunny days. It wasn't just the happy people; all familiar landmarks had suddenly become viewpoints, triggering memories in panoramic that had to be avoided. I couldn't bear to bring his face to mind (although I was simultaneously panicking that actually I couldn't remember him). It was best that I didn't infect others with my sad, bitter self, and I retreated from the summer. The only times I ventured out were to walk the dog, or visit his flat.

The living room was exactly as he'd left it, *The Observer* on the arm of the sofa. His diary and a BFI newsletter on the coffee table. The bedroom was the least habitable room; I sat on the edge of his bed, my head full of his eyes on that morning as I studied the floor – the carpet had been ripped out, and it was as if the room had shrunk. I anticipated that the flat would need to be cleared. I went round photographing it, conscious of taking steps to preserve my memories of his place and the time we spent there, and confused by the irony that once outside the flat, I didn't want to remember anything. As I moved from room to room making pictures, I touched and held objects, like his razor, before photographing them, as if his fingerprints might somehow bring his life to my fingertips, and I was reminded of Kemal curating his museum to Füsun in Orhan Pamuk's *The Museum of Innocence*. One day I made a cup of tea. I took a spoon from the cutlery drawer and remembered how, as we tucked into salmon one evening, he had put his knife and fork down, and said *it's a while since I've found eating so pleasurable; it makes me want to buy some nice cutlery*. I photographed the open drawer.

Being there in John's flat made me feel guilty, all over again, that I hadn't broken my father's door down in the last months of his life. In my dreams he's looking for his house, wondering why we sold it. Or I'm staying with him, and he's not drinking, and we're in his living room talking about something, and he's standing with his hand on his hip, gazing off into space, considering my reply. I wake up smelling him; his voice could have been next door, rather than seventeen years ago.

After such a dream, I turn curator and examine the artifacts, of what I have left: his multicoloured, woven fabric wallet – I like to hold it in my hands as he would have done, to open it and take out his driving license or the scrap of faded orange paper torn from one of the carbon notebooks that my parents used to take orders from at their restaurant, on it is his pin number; his black Filofax type address book, filled with familiar and unfamiliar names, written in his handwriting that definitely bears resemblance to my own; two suitcases chokka with photographs, and press cuttings and letters; his Director's viewfinder; a couple of scripts he wrote; his vinyl collection; a wooden ruler; some pencils; his boat's anchor and compass; a palm tree; a few books; a framed photograph of him and me on Degree day at Lampeter – it was the first time I'd been at an event with both parents, and Emily, *as a family*, since I was five years old, we're standing in front of Old Building; there's love and pride on his face, and I also see how drawn he looks; I can't look at the photograph closely for long. My father's image had jostled with John's when I dialled 999.

*

Body synchronized with mind in the aftermath of John's death: I spun with vertigo, contracted a mystery nausea and projectile vomiting disorder that lasted several months, and then caught shingles. If I tried to write my head felt weighty and full, as if my brain was filled with an ever-expanding ball, with no space for thought. Fiction, like music, and the world outside, was a dangerous, no-go area. The memories of conversations we had shared about novels, poetry or songs were too painful. Life and death experiences of others, however, were soothing. I learnt from Henry Marsh in *Do No Harm*, and *Admissions*, about the complexities of brain tumours and the potentially catastrophic implications of surgery. Poor John clearly had had no chance. But he still needn't have died the way he did. I turned to writers who have shared their agonies in grief that, as Julian Barnes described in *Levels of Life*, are at once *banal and unique*. Joan Didion, in *The Year of Magical Thinking*, took me up into the high altitudes of *complicated grief*, recording the year following her husband's death (and the inherent end of a forty-year marriage) that coincided with her daughter's life-threatening illness. And then I revisited Sonali Deraniyagala's *Wave*, a memoir that had had a profound effect on me when I read it, shortly after its publication in 2013.

Wave journeys into Deraniyagala's apocalyptic *knocked-down world*,[72] detailing the reconstruction of her memories in the aftermath of the 2004 Sri Lankan Tsunami that stole her husband, Steve Lissenburgh; their two sons, seven-year-old Vikram and five-year-old Malli; her parents; a close friend – and her identity. Given my compulsion to visit John's flat, my desperate need to be in his environment, the thematic and metaphorical structure of *Wave*, built on perception of house and home, took on a deeper resonance. It is through description of visits to her family/parental home in Colombo and to her North London house (which she shared with her husband and sons) that, as Deraniyagala dares to remember, she breathes life into her lost family. This stress on home demonstrates, of course, Deraniyagala's sense of terrible displacement.

The family is spending Christmas at a hotel in Yala, Sri Lanka. On Boxing Day morning the kids are playing with their presents; Steve is in the bathroom, and Sonali is chatting to her friend when they notice the sea *coming in*. Normality dissolves into rapidity, short sentences blast from nowhere like the wave that is upon

---

72   Sonali Deraniyagala, *Wave* (Great Britain: Virago, 2013), p.11

them. They flee in a safari jeep. Its interior frames the final portrait of the family together; each parent clasps a child on their lap, before the vehicle is swallowed by the wave. The family is *dispersed*. We see Deraniyagala, *all curled up* foetus-like, she feels herself *spinning*, *being dragged*, her body *whipping backwards and forwards*[73] through the *plummeting* water; the crushing pain in her chest is the pain of drowning. Her recollections are reminiscent of Juliane Koepcke's[74] in her memoir, *When I Fell From The Sky*. Koepcke falls from a plane hit by lightning over the Amazonian jungle:

> My mother is no longer at my side and I'm no longer in the
> airplane ... At an altitude of about ten thousand feet, I'm alone.
> And I'm falling, slicing through the sky ...[75]

And

> I felt as if the rainforest were coming towards me in circles ...
> I was simply spinning ... Even as I was plummeting and fully
> conscious, saw the jungle whirling under me, I was completely
> aware of what was happening to me.[76]

The speed with which both women hurtle towards their respective dismantled worlds is hauntingly similar. Caruth, echoing Freud, writes,

---

73 Deraniyagala, *Wave*, p.9

74 Koepcke's memoir – *When I Fell From The Sky*, (London: Nicholas Brealey Publishing, 2012) – is structured around the 24 December 1971 LANSA plane crash in the Amazonian jungle; seventeen-year-old Juliane is the only survivor (her mother had been travelling with her).

75 Koepcke, *When I Fell From The Sky*, preface xii

76 Koepcke, *When I Fell From The Sky*, p.70

The trauma of the accident, its very unconsciousness, is borne by an act of departure.[77]

Koepcke lands in a tree, in the middle of the jungle, dressed in the flimsiest of clothes, missing one of her sandals and her glasses; with a broken collarbone, severe concussion, and wounds that are soon infested with maggots, not knowing the fate of her mother. Deraniyagala 'lands' on the ground, in the Yala jungle, spitting blood,

> I saw the toppled trees everywhere … trees on the ground with their roots sticking up. What is this swamp? … What is this knocked-down world? The end of time? …[78]

Deraniyagala is left adrift in her knocked-down world, the Armageddon of her inner world with its disfigured memories. In the early aftermath, the only place she felt secure was in the rubble of the Yala hotel:

> Nothing was normal here … I didn't have to shrink from everyday details that were no longer ours … my surroundings were as deformed as I was. I belonged here.[79]

She traces large *footprints of rooms* where they had stayed:

> I lay on the warm floor of our hotel room as a slow moon scaled above the sea, and I could breathe.[80]

---

77   Cathy Caruth, *Unclaimed Experience,* (USA: The John Hopkins University Press,1996) p.22

78   Deraniyagala, *Wave,* pp.11–12

79   Deraniyagala, *Wave,* p.61

80   Deraniyagala, *Wave,* p.65

She wanders through a ghost town, visiting and revisiting the two houses that were once so full of her life, their lives, and that are now her museums. Both houses, her parents' in Colombo – the house in which she grew up, which Steve and the boys loved – and their house in North London increasingly provide her with the comfort that she experienced in the rubble, they encourage her to remember.

When we first see Sonali in her parents' house, it has been cleared of all their belongings; *empty and vast, bereft*, she scours the house *for some atom* of their life and is enraged when her brother rents it out to a Dutch family, whom, at the height of her grieving insanity – and high on pills and alcohol – she delights in harassing; to her fury they stay. Fast-forward two years and the house is empty again; *it cringes with neglect* but now she is curator, reviving both her parents and their things room by room,

> Now, in this house, I can bring my parents close. For six years
> I've pushed them and their death to the fringes of my heart.
> That's all I could tolerate, my focus was on our boys and Steve.
> How hideous, that there should be pecking order in my grief.[81]

The midway point in *Wave*, Part Four, is devoted to Deraniyagala's visiting the North London house for the first time, in 2008. Unlike her parents' house, this home is teeming with their life. Everything is as they left it, down to unopened Christmas presents that were waiting for the boys' return from Sri Lanka. At first, she had wanted the house *destroyed*, later she *needed the assurance that it would be there … preserved.*[82] Here, her work as curator is less abstract; each room brims with artefacts …

---

81 Deraniyagala, *Wave*, p.147

82 Deraniyagala, *Wave*, p.85

Malli's silver tiara, Vik's handwritten cricket score charts, Steve's eyelash on his pillow; then there are the incidental things ... *the medicine spoon that looks like it was used last night, with crystals of Nurofen syrup.*[83] Every little thing induces memory, flashbacks that delineate her family's character. These are foundations on which she builds; in Part Eight, she wants to be in their kitchen *late on a Saturday morning as Steve walks in with a paper bag filled with bagels for lunch.*[84] This evokes a series of recollections that projects Brick Lane; a Sunday lunch for twenty cooked by Steve; the farmers' market in Palmers Green, where they bought artichokes that Steve would steam; France, where Steve kept his lorry driver father company on the road and where he first had artichoke; Wing Yip Supermarket; Billingsgate Fish Market; and finally back to their study and elevenses. So, by remembering the kitchen and bagels, Deraniyagala brings alive the family's passion for food, Steve, and their relationship, and their desire to make every minute count. It's a long way from,

They are my world. How do I make them dead?[85]

and

I must stop remembering ... I shoved away stories of them[86]

There can be no neat, redemptive ending to *Wave*. Deraniyagala reflects:

---

83 Deraniyagala, *Wave*, p.88

84 Deraniyagala, *Wave*, p.165

85 Deraniyagala, *Wave*, p.34

86 Deraniyagala, *Wave*, p.44

> Seven years on and their absence has expanded. Just as our life would have in this time, it has swelled ... I am without them, as much as I am on my own.[87]

She leaves us, though, with an understanding, that's developed over the seven years, that she can only *recover* herself if she keeps her family *near*, and the book closes with a vivid memory etched with love of her *three silly boys* up to high-jinx in the garden, at her expense, to the soundtrack of their laughter.

I gave *Wave* to several friends as soon as I finished it, the first time round. It was, to me, an important book, and one I thought, rather self-righteously, that everyone should read. When I told people about it, the common response was ... *Oh how terrible! I can't even imagine! ... No, no I can't read it, just too sad.* This infuriated me. For no one is exonerated from natural disaster, trauma, or death. It is never that far away from any of us. It is testament, of course, to the quality of Deraniyagala's writing, and her honesty that makes the uprooted trees of her knocked-down world indeed imaginable, and her work to *recover* herself life affirming. *Wave* shone a light during those dark summer months after John died. At the time, I worried that my empathy was presumptuous. After all, I was nursing a hairline fracture of a little toe in comparison to her crushed skeleton.

*

Every day the ginger sits fractionally smaller and lighter in the palm of my hand. It reminds me of how, in grief, we are forensic experts, curating and scrutinising evidence of overlapped existence. And using the tweezers of magical thinking, we

---

87   Deraniyagala, *Wave*, pp.207–8

carefully separate memories to clean them up until they are so brightly tangible it's as if we can just step back into them, and reality – as it was then – will be restored. And the memories *are* so real, and utterly illusory.

Chapter Nineteen

Monday morning. Innnnnn ouuuuuut innnnnn ouuuuuut, breathing slowly; building energy to make a return visit to the mirror and confront my reflection, *at the end of the week I'll be home. Have to be independent by then* ... A knock and a flurry of white coats interrupts this lecture-to-self – The Pain Team.

'Harriet, we've had word that you'll be leaving us shortly,' says Miss Green, standing slightly in front of two other members.

'Yes,' I say, 'Saturday.'

'Brilliant news. It's been a long haul. I'm sure you can't wait to see the back of this place.' She pushes her fingers through her fringe, still the spitting image of my games teacher. 'How's the pain now, on that scale of one to ten?'

'With the pump I get a few hours' peace. Then, around seven.'

'That's what we guessed,' she says, nodding. 'So, it's important that you stay on the OxyNorm when you get home, since you seem to be tolerating it well ... We'll remove your IV later today, and start you on the tablet form. Exactly the same dosage and every four hours.'

'How long for?'

'Possibly for another six weeks. It's an extremely effective drug. Best not to stay on it for too long, though. The opioid content makes it addictive. Equally, you mustn't suddenly stop taking it, we'll gradually decrease the dose.'

This surprises me; I don't feel wooziness or any effect other than partial pain relief when I use the pump.

'And, of course, keep taking it in tandem with the paracetamol. You're welcome to call us with any questions when you're home.' The three of them smile at me before leaving the room almost as abruptly as they entered. I barely have time to digest what they've said before there's another knock at the door and a woman with a clipboard enters.

'Hello, you must be Harriet?' She comes over to shake my hand, brown curls tripping over the collar of her blouse.

'I'm Karen and I'm an occupational therapist,' she says, sitting in the blue chair. 'I hear you're off home soon?'

'Yes, I am.'

'How are you feeling about that?'

'Excited.' I'd like to expand on this but I'm stuck for words again.

Karen nods and smiles.

'Any apprehension?'

'No.'

'Because having had such a long stay in hospital, it would be perfectly natural if you did have some concerns.'

'I don't think I'm ... um ... um ... in ... um in ...'

'Institutionalised?'

'Thank you, that's the word.'

'Great. But don't be surprised if you do become a little anxious.'

'Alright.' I'm puzzling over what specifically might make me worried about going home.

'What are you most looking forward to?'

Is this a trick question? 'Um ... being in my own bed ... walking the dog ...'

'Oh, what kind of dog do you have?'

'A whippet ... Harvey.'

'A friend of mine has one, Lola. She's delightful. So fast. At home she curls up into the tiniest bundle.'

'They're 90mph couch potatoes.'

'So, your goal, Harriet is to be out walking Harvey, soon as you can?' Karen says, scribbling something down on her clipboard.

'Yes,' I say. It's dawning on me that goals are, of course, the way forward.

'My goals,' she says, 'are to facilitate your transition from hospital to home so that you return to independence and walking Harvey as quickly as it's healthily possible.'

'What will that ... involve.' Involve was not the word I was hunting for, but it'll do.

'I'd like to make an appointment for you to come down to the Occupational Therapy Centre, it's on the ground floor of the hospital, maybe in a couple of days so I can run through a few things with you and perhaps sort you out with some goodies to make life easier at home.'

'Like what?'

'Tell me about your bed at home, Harriet.'

'It's a double.'

Karen smiles. 'How do you find getting in and out of bed at the moment?'

'Fine ... takes time, though.'

'It might be that we can fix your bed up with some cot rails, for example.' She laughs at my expression.

'They'd just help with giving you some temporary support, and we certainly don't want you falling anywhere.' She gets up from the chair, 'So, I'll come and collect you in a couple of days, I'll let Sister know when, okay, Harriet?'

'Okay,' I say.

*

I flex the fingers on both of my cannula-free hands and show them off to Natasha.

'We're taking a hike today,' she says, waving me through the doorway and on to the long blue corridor, 'so it's very cool we don't have to bother about the IV stand anymore ... that's good walking, Harriet ... keep your head up.'

This is the first time I've walked out of the confines of my room. The nurses' station comes into view. I don't recognise any of the faces that are smiling at me as I shuffle past with the Zimmer.

'Go girl!'

But I know that honeyed voice. Maria. Back from holiday. Where is she? There, across the corridor, standing in the entrance of another room. She waves and I stop to wave back.

'Okay. Ready to try without this now?' says Natasha in front of me, with one hand on the frame. I take a deep breath.

'Sure,' I say. She takes the Zimmer. And I'm just standing there.

'One foot in front of the other, that's all it is ...'

One step. Wobbly. Two steps. Very wobbly. All that space in front of me. The mirror. The hunched, feral creature staring back at me.

'That's better, you're standing much straighter, and I like the smile, Harriet.'

My body's all over the place. My arms flap out to the sides; fingers spread, outstretched, like balance antennae. I am walking unaided. A penguin. With an acre of a smile, in spite of *myself*. My heart racing. We get to the end of the corridor, to the doors.

'Next time,' she says. 'We'll go back to your room now ... here, you've done well,' and she proffers the Zimmer.

'No, it's okay,' I say, and flap the distance back to the blue chair.

*

'Sit on the bench … there, I've got you … now swing your legs over, one at a time… that's right, good girl … now, take some deep breaths … how are the black spots? … okay, now when you're ready, grip the bar, there on the wall, no, with both hands … that's right, now pull yourself up, slowly though … alright? … Great! Is the pain okay? … Now keep holding on to the bar and I'll turn on the shower … okay? If you feel funny just sit down again, but slowly … there, how's the water? … Is the temperature okay?' I had viewed the agency nurse, Stella, and her warmth with some trepidation, Harry Potter and the Case of the Missing Phone still fresh in my mind.

'So you've got me for the day,' she'd said, changing my long surgical stockings for the first time in five weeks, 'tell me if I pinch you,' she said, easing the stretch fabric up over each knee with thumbs and forefingers '… there, now is there anything you'd like me to help with today?'

'Um, if you've time, I'd um appreciate help in the bathroom … I'm going home in a few days and haven't really used it yet.'

Within half an hour I was settled on the loo while she waited outside the door, until black ink blots in front of my eyes got the better of my attempts and she rescued me from passing out. Then, after arranging my pillows perfectly, like origami, she left me to rest. A couple of hours later, as I stand shaky in the shower, the mega-gratitude I feel for this dose of Stella's kindness dwarfs the embarrassment of my nakedness. My stomach protrudes in the most unnatural of ways, as if the skin could slit any second now, and I picture an overly ripened peach that splits to a fly-feeding frenzy. How can Mr Winkler think the haematoma has reduced in size? I hold my upturned palms out in front of me and watch the shower-stream bounce off them like mercury balls. My ears are all over the gush and splash of the water, tailing each rivulet; restocking my sound library. I step forward but instantly recoil as the jets staple-gun my tummy.

'Careful, Harriet. Remember, slow movements. Here, sit back down on the bench for a moment,' Stella says, passing me some soap. She reaches for the showerhead and pulls it round to the back of my neck.

'I don't think we'll wash your hair,' she says. *Okay.* Warm water runs down my back, my eyes flit to the dressing gown that Emily brought me hanging on the bathroom door, and I remember how I felt its softness on the day she gave it to me. Of the lifetime of showers I've had, have I ever truly experienced the very second that water meets skin as I am experiencing it now? It's a piece of paradise, as close as I've been to those idyllic, tropical waterfalls you see in advertisements.

'Sit down to dry yourself, I'll be right outside if you need me.'

I pat myself with the towel, feeling in turn revolted – *Forget the haematoma, guys. It's definitely a monster in there* – and protective of my stomach, and pull on the mini-nightie that Emily's mother-in-law sent me. It's taupe with silky lace edging the low neckline and the sleeveless arms, sophisticated sexy. *Like wearing a bikini while trekking the North Pole*, I think, holding on to the basin, looking at my reflection in the mirror. The garment makes me feel better; it tones down the bruising on my neck and softens the jut of bone. I smooth down my hair, no brush to hand. Then clean my teeth. I bend slightly to spit out the toothpaste, there's a white flash in the mirror. And I meet my eyes again in the reflection; their expression remains unrecognisable and fearful.

Is it me or my belting heart that pushes open the bathroom door?

'Feel better?' says Stella, smiling.

'Yes,' I say, talking over the blood-beating drum in my ears, 'thank you so much, for your help.'

'It's what I'm here for. Now, let's get those circulation stockings back on again ... yes, on the bed, you must be tired.'

I am able to build on Stella's kindness, and no longer need to carry out my morning ablutions in bed. Every action is in slo-mo with glimpses of independence waiting round the corner.

*

Natasha and I walk to the end of the corridor. She presses the security buzzer for the door to open.

'Just round that corner, past the lifts.'

I spot signage to Outpatients, and another ward, 15 South; people walk by, I don't look at their faces, every step requires meticulous concentration. Round the corner and there, standing oddly alone, is a doll's house staircase. Three steps up to a platform and then three stairs down again.

'Hold on to the handrail. One step up, so both feet meet ... that's right. And repeat.'

'Feels unnatural. Can't I walk up them as normal?'

'If you're not feeling too shaky, go for it!'

'Only out of breath.'

'It's not surprising. You've had a collapsed lung, been off your feet for over a month, plus there's everything else with the angiomyolipoma. It's gonna take time to get fit.'

'And my legs? They're still heavy, the dragging feeling ...'

Huffing and puffing. Seeking far too much reassurance. But going up and down these little stairs feels great.

'Also to be expected. A lot of it is pressure on your sciatic nerve. It'll improve as the haematoma reduces.'

'So long as it's all normal.'

'Look at you! You've been up and down this staircase five times already. Sweet as. You've surpassed my expectations this week.'

*

At 10 p.m. there's a new, waspish blood-thinning injection in my stomach, and two spooky blue pills that smell of cyanide almond. Less than five minutes after swallowing the minute tablets, *smaller than hole-punch chad*, I've been coshed into a heavy sleep that shuts down even the sucking stare of a gargoyle. I'm out for about three hours; at half past one my eyes spring open, scouring the room and the night sky, as if I've fallen asleep on some surveillance assignment. They're not sleeping pills. 'I've written you up for Amitriptyline,' Mr Winkler had said, 'I'm hoping it'll combat the electric pain. It helps treat nerve-ending discomfort, which I suspect, in your case, is being caused by scarring from the embolisation.' I visualised those nerve endings as naked winter treetops silhouetted against the whitest sky and had put them under a macro lens, a cluster of branches, and yes, there I saw the yellowish puckered skin of scarring, throttling the flow of blood, in gasping spasms.

Footsteps approaching, several people, among them the patter of lighter steps.

'Hat! Hattyroona!'

'Girls! Don't run. Be gentle with Hat. Remember what I said.'

Alice and Maddy screech to a cartoon halt in front of my chair, a tangle of pink, orange, purple and blue ...

... New Year's Eve in Ferryside. Just three months ago. They are wearing anoraks, hats and scarves in those same colours; *Look left, look right! All clear ... no trains!* They scamper across the

railway track that zippers up the River Towy estuary. Ferryside is
the penultimate stop on the Cardiff–Carmarthen route, the train
journey that so captivated me all those years ago, on the day of
my interview at Lampeter. The tide is out; we sit on rocks, hands
dipping into popcorn still warm from the pan, and watch the dogs
chasing one another, looping out to the water's edge. I pour hot
chocolate from the thermos into picnic mugs. Their eyes bright,
cheeks rosy; Alice's hair flaming in the fading light. Afterwards
we crouch in the sand, collecting shells to the trill and whistle of
worm-hooking curlews.

'Hat?' they say.

'Hi!' I say, reaching out for my nieces. Both of them take a step
back, unsure.

'Honestly, they've been so excited,' Emily says, her ponytail
swinging, 'thought they were going to bounce out of the car.' She
raises her eyebrows.

'To see you in hospital,' nods five-year-old Maddy, annunciating
each of hospital's three syllables with deliberation, 'are you feeling
better, Hat?' She looks me up and down with those lake eyes.

'Yes, Madz, I really am.'

'Mummy says we're not allowed to kiss you, Hat ... in case
we give you lurgies. You can have this instead,' Alice hands me
a unicorn, 'he's going to magic you even more better, even more
quickly, every day.'

I brush the fluffy white beast against my cheek.

'Alice, that's very generous. Won't you miss him? He's one of
your favourites.'

'Snowysnowshine wants to be with you, we've had a long talk
about it.' Her pale cheeks flush, she's pulled the cuffs of her cardi
over her thumbs, and I understand she's serious.

'His little nose is soft as a kitten,' says Maddy, poking the unicorn's velvet muzzle.

'Do you know why Snowysnowshine's ears are silver on the inside?' says Alice, nudging her younger sister's hand away.

'No,' I say.

'It's because,' she says, lowering her voice to a whisper, 'he likes to play in the moonlight.'

'Is that a secret, Alice? Because *everyone* heard you,' says Maddy, dancing around.

'What shall I feed Snowy?' I ask.

'Acorns and clouds ... but he finds them himself.'

'Do clouds taste like candy floss?' I say to the unicorn.

'Noooo,' he neighs and hrumphs, 'mmmmarshmmmmallow.'

Both girls giggle. They still hang back. Normally, Maddy would be clambering all over me. She loves to play with my hair. Emily is sorting out my cupboard.

'Moms is getting everything ship-shape for you at home.'

I smile. 'I can imagine.'

'Do you get nightmares, Hat?'

'Sometimes. Why, Alice?'

'Cos guess what?'

'What, what?'

'Snowy chases nightmares away. He really can.'

I widen my eyes. 'He's going to be jolly useful.'

'Please may I have a go on your bed, Hat?' Maddy's already kicked off her shoes.

'Of course. You can make it go up and down.'

Emily zaps the remote control and the foot of the bed raises, and then the middle of the bed.

'Don't, Mummy!' And she slips off the caterpillar bed as fast as she had jumped onto it.

'Wasn't there something else you wanted to give Hat ... in

my handbag,' my sister winks at Maddy. Both girls race to the bag, which Emily had left by the mini-bar fridge. An A4 envelope lands on my lap.

'We've made very special cards for you.'

'I can see that. Wow. These aren't cards. They're books!' I say, leafing through the folders of coloured paper with flowers tall as houses, treetops tickling the stars, Harvey as daddy longlegs, hearts and kisses. 'What beautiful drawings, such neat handwriting.'

'Right girls, I told you we were just popping in and out, and we've been here twenty minutes. Hattyroona needs to rest.'

She's called it just right. Their visit has been oxygen but Bone-Ache has taken up his tools.

'Next time *we* see you, we can have a midnight feast, can't we, Hat?' says Alice, kissing my shoulder.

'With popcorn and hot chocolate,' says Maddy, kissing my knee.

'And clouds,' hrumphs the unicorn.

Their footsteps and giggling recede down the corridor and quietness seeps in through the shutters. I return to the aptly named Gothic Villa, where we stayed over New Year, and to the kitchen where I'd made the popcorn.

From the window you can see the estuary and, on a clear day, Lansteffan Castle across the water. When the evening's festivities finished that night, and everyone had gone to bed, I stoked the wood burner against the gale that was howling to be let in, and flipped through the CD collection. Among the music lurked a recording of *Under Milk Wood*. My father, a devotee of Dylan Thomas, had given me a poster of the Augustus John portrait for my Lloyd Thom room, in my first year at Lampeter. It went up in the cottage too. I switched off the lamps. The wood burner hatch was open, flames dancing to the draft. I curled up in the leather armchair, under a wool throw. Anthony Hopkins was reading 'First Voice'. The roll of his delivery, the words and their images, the storm beating at the window and the fire lulled me.

'Call me Tony,' Hopkins said when we were introduced. *Get a grip*, I told my somersaulting heart, swooning to the stranglehold of those killer-blue eyes, and shook his hand. His broad, magnificent hand.

He had been awarded an Honorary Fellowship from the English Department at Lampeter the same year that I graduated, shortly after his Oscar for *The Silence of the Lambs*. A couple of years later, in 1996, I received a letter from the university ... *We understand that you are a photographer and as a graduate of Lampeter we would very much like you to cover the opening of our new Clifford Tucker Theatre by Sir Anthony Hopkins ...*

'Can I come as your assistant?' Jocelyn joked when I read the letter to him over the phone. The two of us had gone down. He hadn't been able to resist barking apertures at me on the occasions he had been in earshot.

A crowd of about two hundred students gathers in a semicircle, pinioning us to the theatre wall, bloodthirsty for an autograph. Hopkins has just stepped down from the lectern after a ninety-minute Q&A that had delved into his roots and pecked at demons. He'd obliged one interrogator with the notorious Hannibal Lecter suck of his lips, as if he had just devoured a liver.

In between signing the notebooks and scraps of paper thrust his way, Hopkins turns to me. 'Are you okay with this? I imagine it might be daunting if you're not used to it?' *The way he seals his Ts.*

'Me? Oh, I'm fine,' I say. I am *way* more than okay; I am *way* more than ecstatic to be forced into pore-counting proximity of my favourite actor. To have him chatting to me. For goodness' sake, I even wrote about his *Silence of the Lambs* performance in an essay on Bernard Malamud's *The Fixer*.

'Good, good,' he says over the gabbling hullabaloo, 'get some nice shots?'

I nod coolly – or what I deem to be in a cool manner, hoping I haven't made him look too much of a politician by focusing on his hands. They had been irrepressible in the Q&A, so much movement and emphasis; as if counteracting the constraints put upon him by his suit. (Which is sharp, he brushes up well.) *There's a restlessness about him, an uncontainable energy.* The pictures inside the auditorium will be black-and-white grainy, I hadn't wanted to use flash and opted instead for TMAX 3200; I wanted that texture. I'd taken some shots of him in The Old Building's quadrangle with the Principal too, but I had yet to get the full-face portrait. That would be for my portfolio. *Gotta ask soon.*

'Would you have time for one more picture, outside, afterwards?'

'Absolutely.'

And then here I am, standing with my camera inches from his nose. The background is incidental because his face fills the frame. His eyes glitter down the lens. Nice and dark. *Click.*

'I was *so* nervous.'

'Nonsense, Harri. You were grinning like a Cheshire cat all day,' said Jocelyn as we climbed Sugar Loaf Mountain on our way back to London. He evidenced this with a portrait of his own – Hopkins with his arm round me, an indelible smile plastered over my face. Standing pillow-end of Daddy's bloodied bed, I'd noticed Jocelyn's print was still there, framed, on his wall.

I put another log on the fire.

And think back to our afternoon on the estuary beach, to the train that had clattered by as the girls and I collected shells. When I had glanced up, I'd thought again of my eighteen-year-old self on her way to the interview. Imagined her as one of those faces looking out of the window, watching a whippet and a retriever career along the driftwood-aplenty beach, and a woman playing with two little girls. I thought of the assumptions she would have undoubtedly made.

The door on Gothic Villa closes. Scenes from *Under Milk Wood* distract me from the gnawing in my legs and back. I magpie down to the *green lathered trees* of Llareggub Hill and pinch their leaves for my velvety stash of verdancy. But Gothic Villa returns: it had been in front of the wood burner that I decided to let my fortieth birthday, twenty-six days round the corner, slide by without a whisper. *See. All my work is payback for such self-indulgence*, whittles away Bone-Ache.

*

Knock knock.

'Hi, Harriet … how are you? All set?' Karen pushes a wheelchair into the room. She's wearing a uniform today, navy trousers and white tunic, like the physiotherapists. Her movements are quick; I sense that she's in a rush.

'That's right, feet on the footrests. Going to pop this blanket over you, oops better tuck it in, don't want it getting caught in the wheels, do we?' The wheelchair is about as sturdy as an umbrella with a faulty folding mechanism, and one that's missing several spokes.

'Sorry if the ride's a bit jerky, this chair's seen better days,' she says, reading my mind and pushing me into the corridor and past the nurses' station at a Ferrari gallop. I hold on to the handgrips, my knuckles like mountain ranges. Through the doors at the end, to the lifts.

'Okay, Harriet?' as the lift plummets to the ground floor. The doors open. On to a throng of midriffs, of varying proportions. My eyes travel up their bodies. Patients, doctors, nurses, visitors, waiting for the lift. I spy tall greetings-card stands that are pillars of a kiosk; tables, chairs and the Costa Coffee logo; escalators against a wall of stained glass – Miro-esque geometrical shapes, swirling blues and purples; people chatting, laughing, thoughtful expressions, sad eyes; we navigate through it all and whizz down a maze of white corridors.

First off, she parks me in the office.

'Hi Dom, this is Harriet,' Karen says to the grey-haired man who's just got off the phone.

'Hello Harriet, welcome to our chaotic abode,' he says. *A kind face.*

'Right, sit tight. I've just got to attend to an urgent admin issue before we get started,' Karen says to me, checking that the chair's brakes are locked.

The room is supernatural in its normality. I gulp down the scene: a couple of desks, each landscaped with avalanching piles of papers and ringed coffee mugs; whiteboards on easels, scrawled with blue and red charts, green arrows dashed here and there; timetables pinned to the wall, even a drawing pin glints as exotically as a rare gem. I watch Karen's and Dom's mouths as they talk, not paying attention to what they're discussing but transfixed by how their words effortlessly flow.

I'm perched on a tall white stool in a mocked-up kitchen. It looked quite uncomfortable, but the seat is cleverly slanted and is invisibly back supportive.

'You could have that in your kitchen, and use it while you wait for the kettle to boil, or when you're chatting with whoever is cooking you something delicious,' Karen suggests with a wink.

'But with the kettle, make sure it contains no more than a mugful of water. That's your weight limit.'

She produces recuperation aid after recuperation aid, demonstrating each with the exaggerated actions and emphatic smile of cabin crew. Even the adapted loo seat. It's like watching a shopping channel, except no buying is involved – everything is hired out at minimal charge by a company associated with the hospital.

The biro is thick in my clumsy fingers as I sign an agreement for the stool, rails for my bed, a raised loo seat, shower bench, shower grab handle ... and the simply ingenious Reacher (a gadget that saves you from bending). 'Don't worry, you'll be calling us to collect them before you know it,' she says, patting my shoulder.

Karen is chatting away ... something about dogs. Hospital life squalls past as we wait for the lift back up to the fifteenth floor. All I've been doing is sitting; it's as if I were queuing for the bus on a Friday evening after a twelve-hours-a-day week. I've been away from my room for exactly an hour and a half.

*

That tomorrow will be my last full day at Charing Cross is stretching my brain. *Today, doh.* Ironically, it is as hard to comprehend as it has been to accept that I needed to be here in the first place. When Mr Winkler first mooted going home, I was tachycardic with anticipation, banners and bunting strung all over my mind. They're still there, fluttering away with echoes of Christmas Eve, or the day before school holidays.

*

'Fancy a cup of tea?'

I look at the badge on the nurse with altitudinous cheekbones. She's just given me some paracetamol. Sister Hesther. It's 2 a.m., the Amitriptyline-sodden sleepiness has worn off. Naomi flashes through my thoughts, *Be an angel ... I'm fair parched.*

'Tea?'

'Of course. I like making my patients a hot drink if they can't sleep,' says Sister Hesther, plumping up the pillows behind my back. 'We haven't met before, have we?' she says as if we had just got chatting at a party. 'And you've been here a while, haven't you?' says Hesther. 'I've been working on 15 South. That's why our paths haven't crossed. So, what's it to be? English Breakfast or peppermint?'

Peppermint zings up my nostrils; tea has never been more decadent. Hesther's unexpected kindness shines alongside Stella's. A sip. Looking at the cinema screen, at the big blue-black out-there, waiting beyond this room, beyond this building. I finally got to press my nose against Boat-Race-view window and lost my balance when I saw the river that I love, and Hammersmith Bridge. They are not my eyes that can't look. They are the eyes that I see in the bathroom mirror. The ones that don't belong to me.

*

'You're my last patient,' says Natasha as we walk towards the mini-steps.

'Today?'

'At Charing Cross, full stop.'

'You're leaving?'

'I have a flight tonight. Back to Auckland. London's been a heck of a trip, truly. But you know, I've missed my family and friends ... yup, let's do six reps of these,' she says as I take hold of the handrail. 'Great, Harriet. It's astonishing. Really. The progress you've made this week.'

'Not having as many white-flash attacks either. Easier to move.' I'm breathing heavily. 'Have you got a job lined up?'

'Yup, I start in ten days. A friend of mine's leaving her position, so I can slot right in. Cool huh? Okay, stop there. Get your breath back.'

'New Zealand. I saw a film ... can't remember the title ... one of my favourite films. It's got um ... sorry, can't even remember the actors. Incredible beach.'

'Oh you mean *The Piano*?'

'Yes! How could I not remember?' Memory is tripping me up more than my heavy legs.

'With Harvey Keitel and Holly Hunter? Yeah. I've walked along that beach. It's choice. Only a forty-minute drive from Auckland. You should visit. Okay, we've finished with *these* steps,' she says, gesturing for me to walk with her. She opens a cupboard-like door along the corridor and snaps on a light. *Woah*. A staircase, at least thirty steps. It smells musty.

'The idea,' Natasha says, 'is not to reach the top, but to practise turning, and to come down again, at about a third of the way up.'

Just concentrate on the step up. And up. And up. I pass a third of the way up and get to about halfway – *easy* – as that's probably the height of the staircase at home. Turn, *easy*. Coming down is slower. My eyes play tricks; the stairs start shifting, like escalators. Back with Natasha, I look up at the distance I've just climbed.

We walk to my room, to the blue chair. She pours some Lucozade and hands it to me. I'm grateful for the sugar hit.

'Good luck, Harriet. You've come such a long way. I feel fortunate to have had you as my last patient.' She takes my hand. 'You're going to be fine.'

'I will. Thank you. For everything,' I say, hoping that she gets the extent of my gratitude. Natasha has been perfect. There were days when she came for our sessions when either I was in too much pain or there was nothing in the energy tank, and she would make the time to fit me in later in the day. Always encouraging, reassuring, and sunny.

*

I am getting closer, I tell those wild eyes, as I stand at the basin.

*

My mother arrives later in the afternoon; she wants to be present for Mr Winkler's evening visit. Every day I have been cheered by her smile; today it is that much broader. And scented.

'You're wearing *Mitsouko*,' I say as she kisses me, suddenly realising that I haven't smelt her perfume for weeks. She's worn it since my father gave it to her, when she was nineteen.

'It's an experiment ... does it bother your nose?'

'Not at all.'

'Maybe your sense of smell is settling down,' she says, decanting stuff from her little freezer bag into the minibar fridge for presumably the last time. 'All your equipment's arrived. Very efficient. They fixed the rails to your bed.'

'Great.' *Hard to be excited about that.* 'The stool?'

'It's in the kitchen.' She looks up at me, worried. 'You're in pain.'

'It's worth it – I climbed stairs.' And while she prepares a snack I tell her about the physio session and how Natasha is heading back to New Zealand.

Sharp knock at the door. Mr Winkler, navy-suited, all blue eyes and beaming smile.

'Hello, hello,' he says, striding over to shake my mother's hand. She half rises from her chair to greet him. 'No, please don't get up. How nice to see you. How are you, Mrs Mercer?' *He's smooth*.

'Delighted that my daughter's coming home, Mr Winkler,' her smile mirroring his own.

'Indeed, finally,' he says, looking at me, 'and how are you feeling today, Harriet?'

'Good, thank you.' My best smile.

'Excited?'

'It's a bit ... unreal. But yes, of course.'

'I'd say the whole thing's been an *extra*ordinary experience, hasn't it? All of it must seem quite unreal. And, it'll feel odd to be out of this environment, for sure.' He gestures around the room. 'May I have a quick look at your tummy? Sorry if my hands are cold ... How's the pain?'

'Under control,' I say.

'I hear you've been making fantastic progress with physio.' His fingers press around my right side, gentle but with purpose. 'It's definitely going down, I know you don't agree.' He grins at my grimace.

'Is that the haematoma reducing, Mr Winkler?' says my mother.

'Hopefully, the blood *is* starting to be reabsorbed,' he says, pulling up a chair.

'And the angiomyolipoma?'

'We'll monitor its size and behaviour of its blood vessels with scans ... perhaps we'll consider using some cancer drugs; it's a case of watch and wait.'

'What exercises should I be doing?' I want to move the discussion away from the angiomyolipoma and on to the subject of recovery.

'I'll see you in two weeks for a CT scan, until then I'd like you to follow pretty much the same routine as here. Potter about by all means, enjoy being home, continue with what you've been doing in physio. Rest.' *Laser stare.* 'And eat!'

'Don't worry Mr Winkler, I'll see to that,' my mother says. 'Are there any symptoms we should be looking out for?'

'Absolutely. There's obviously risk of a re-bleed. I've already warned Harriet. Any nausea, fever, clamminess, or hardening of the stomach and it's ambulance time.'

He stays for a while longer, answering her list of questions. And then he moves his chair neatly back. 'Good luck, Harriet. I'll see you in two weeks.'

When his footsteps have melted into the corridor, my mother post-mortems his visit.

'Thank heavens he came on duty that night,' she says afterwards, hoisting a holdall over her shoulder. 'I'll leave the other one for Emily,' and then she puts it down again to come and give me a kiss. 'Right, Darling, I'll see you tomorrow. At home. How wonderful.' She picks up the bag again, and her handbag, and is almost out the door before she comes back for Little Leopard-Faced Orchid, still in bloom.

'Text me when you get home,' I say, as I've said every night.

Lovely Hesther brings more peppermint tea after my 2 a.m. paracetamol. I settle down to the remaining hours of entertaining my wakeful head. At home, this babysitting won't be necessary, I'll be able to sleep in my own bed. I won't be sitting upright. I won't need the bedside light on all night. The gargoyles are diminishing: they're powerless against the first flush of Amitriptyline; now, when I close my eyes, there are a few minutes of lava-lamp orangeness before the wall takes shape. A brick beckons; on examination it begins to crumble, from the middle outwards. I jump to another brick, not waiting for it to morph into gargoyle eyes, or fingers, and then to another and another and so on, until there are no more. Each hollowed brick is like the window of a derelict apartment block; I open my eyes, choosing not to peer in and risk confrontation with the gnarly squatters.

Everything is in its place on the over-bed table: phone, tissues, lip balm, ginger ale, Lucozade. The room appears empty, almost as if I have already left. Yet, it had hardly been decked out with belongings. Apart from a plant. Studying and admiring the features of Little-Leopard-Faced-Orchid – so closely that I fancy I even heard its gentle chuff on occasion – has played a consuming part in my nightly routine

Up to the clock face. *All aboard!* Legs astride the hour hand, clutching it, I pull myself along, inching forward. At the very tip, I stand up, teetering on this tightrope – I don't have crow toes to grip, and Charles Blondin I'm not.

Close up: 1 2 3 4 5 6 7 8 9 10 11 12: dust drifts on their lines and curves. *You'd need a snow shovel to clear just one particle, of time.*

I slip, and land – with the plump thud of a conker – back on my bed.

'You can't do that,' sneers Bone-Ache.

'Oh, but I just did.'

My eyes turn to the window. The biggest luxury, apart from privacy, of moving up to the fifteenth floor has been this cinema screen: I sit back for its final performance, of Dawn disentangling herself from the embrace of Night, layer by gauzy layer.

*

There's a plink in the washbasin mid-teeth-brush. I fish out half a tooth before it's swallowed by the plug swirl. My tongue probes the broken victim. Last summer it had endured root canal treatment.

'You had surgery, right?' says the nurse. 'It must've taken a knock when they put you under.'

'A small price to pay,' I say, a cramped room and concerned faces crowding in:

'Harriet, we need to put a tube in your neck, it might feel a bit odd … okay … Right, time to go. Try not to worry; we're going to look after you. You're going to feel sleepy now. Take a nice deep breath.'

Getting dressed for the first time since Sunday, 9 March. Today is Saturday, 26 April. Pulling on trackpants bought yesterday by my mother has never taken so long. The XL waistband fits my alien stomach; my skin is yelling, *BUT it's lined with the incisors of a piranha*. I'm quite exhausted and stick to layering the trackpants with my nightie and oversized sweatshirt that I cannot be bothered to change.

A woman with spiky purple hair walks into the room.

'Harriet? Hi, I'm Jenny,' she says, coming to shake my hand, 'Mr Winkler's PA … is it okay if I have a seat?'

'Please do.'

'I should be at home with the grandchildren but I've got that much to do. And I didn't want you to leave before I introduced myself … I like putting a face to a name, do you know what I mean?'

'Yes. I do.' I can't take my eyes off her hair, it's spectacular.

'How are you now?'

'So much better, thank you.'

'That's good to hear. I know you had people worried.'

She tells me about her grandchildren and her plans for them this weekend. Then she glances down at her watch. 'How are you getting home?'

'My sister should be here soon.'

'I won't keep you then. Ooh, I nearly forgot to give you this,' she takes an envelope out of her handbag and puts it on the over-bed table, next to my phone, 'it's your discharge letter and also a date from Imaging, for your CT scan.'

'Thank you,' I say, 'and for coming to say hello.'

'Not at all, Harriet. Any worries, please don't hesitate to ring. The numbers are all there,' she says, pointing to the letter.

'Ready then?' Emily arrives, her face brimming with expectation. I sense that she's about to pop with the excitement for both of us. She kisses my cheek. 'It's home time, Sissy!'

'Just a couple of bits and bobs to put in there.' I point to the remaining holdall.

'Mustn't forget these,' she says, and jumps on the bed to take down all my cards from the cubicle frame. The nurse comes in to take my obs for the last time and to present me with a sealed bag, chocker with medication: fat orange, white and mauve boxes of OxyNorm, skinny ones of Amitriptyline. 'The dosage instructions are all on the boxes, any questions call the ward. Sister will phone tomorrow, to see how you're getting on, okay? Right, I've called a porter to take you down when you're ready.' And with a clipped smile, she disappears.

'Wow. She was beautiful. And perfunctory,' Emily says, scurrying round the room, looking under this and that to check that nothing's been missed.

No familiar faces are present as the porter wheels me past the nurses' station and to the swing door, held open by my sister. The wheelchair feels a lot more substantial than Karen's one. As we enter the lift I catch sight of the mini-staircase. Down to the ground floor. Something that I'm unable to define is welling in my chest.

'That's where we waited to pounce on Mr Winkler at lunchtimes, when you were in Critical Care,' Emily says, pointing to the packed Costa. She's walking ahead, at some lick – accelerating, as if she cannot wait to get out of the building, bags hoiked over her shoulder, her hair long and shiny.

A revolving door. Seconds later I'm putting my hands up to shade my eyes from the dazzling sun.

'And that's where Naomi went for her smokes,' Emily says, gesturing to the water feature across the path, opposite the hospital entrance where, sure enough, dressing-gowned patients, some with IV stands, huddle together over their cigarettes. I picture Naomi among them, in her sleeveless nightie.

Chapter Twenty

Fay's Crew: A Buen Camino

The track is gap-toothed: slabs of stone, felted with moss, bound with ivy and monumental as gravestones, mark the way as it winds deep into ancient oak forest. I stop for a moment and listen to the birdsong. Undergrowth stirs, twigs crack, and there's a trickle of waterfall; I breathe in the muskiness rising from the forest floor. Fog has stripped off to a scanty mist and ghosts about the trees. I feel its dampness on my skin, and its vapour puffs fluorescence into every shade of green. Some trees are waist high in bramble and fern, others are giants, ankle deep in foliage. They've stepped out of Spenser's *Faerie Queene*, branches bend at the elbow and clasp gnarled foreheads in anguish, others are legs – turned to tree in mid-stride; hollows scream darkly from trunks.[88] – *Samos, Galicia, on the Camino de Santiago, 8 September 2013*

When I finally arrived in Arca, white sky fell around hunched, pallid buildings, and although my backpack felt heavy after the day's walk, I hurried through the deserted streets, pole clacking on pavement, impatient for an alleyway that would lead into old-

---

88 From my own notebook, on the Camino de Santiago.

town charm. The afternoon before I had been blissfully lost in a labyrinth of backstreets in Arzúa, and had stopped to admire a front door – with a sculptural brass knocker – when it creaked open. Out of the house stepped a woman, about eighty, barely five foot tall, in a blue gingham housecoat leading a creamy, crescent-horned cow. She spoke to her charge in a low voice, the rope hung loose around the animal's neck. I continued down the street, but was so struck by the surrealism that I doubled back and followed them in the direction from which I came. The woman was only centimetres taller than her cow and there was a sweet symmetry in their companionable amble: both broad of beam, black slippers padding in time with black hooves. They turned into a narrow cobbled street where a smell of onions frying emanated from one of the terraced houses; the clopping hooves echoed, and the swing of udder was increasingly pendulous. We passed an *horreo*, doors painted red under its overhanging roof, and squeezed down another street. At the end of it was a house with an attached barn, into which they disappeared, the woman still talking to the cow in a reassuring and affectionate tone. The Second Act was a spectacular sunset and a smile had played on my face all evening. No such magic in Arca; any vestige of character had been sucked from its cheeks. I checked out cafes and bars in preparation for the evening, several were closed; those that were open looked fairly anaemic. Still, there was at least a supermarket where I spotted a row of Queso Tetilla, the breast-shaped Galician cheese I'd been hankering to try since Portomarin, and I picked up a bag of almonds too.

The town's sapped colour had evidently been poured directly into the garish purple frieze that edged the walls of my room in the B&B. I sat on the bed, tried to ignore the lime bedspread and dismiss sulky thoughts, that here I was, on the penultimate evening of my Camino walk, staying in a town that could be called Literally Anywhere. After giving myself a talking to, *you're sounding like a spoilt brat*, I showered, and prepared for an evening in, editing photos and updating my notebook. The moment pen nosed paper, a commotion began. Slamming of doors. Loud Irish voices. Raucous laughter. Irritation reappeared and I opened my door, ready to politely request that the party might pipe down. The doors of the bedrooms opposite were flung wide open. Eight women in various stages of undress; backpacks half unpacked, garments strewn everywhere, it was as if I was looking into my niece Alice's bedroom ... *We're getting ready to go out. So sorry! We've been making a dreadful din, haven't we?* said one. *A royal racket*, agreed the curly-white-haired lady sitting very upright on one of the beds. *That's why the boys have chosen to sleep downstairs! Yes, indeed! There's more of us!* said another. *We're walking to celebrate Fay's eightieth, can you believe it, eighty years old and walking the Camino de Santiago?* chipped in the sole brunette, glass of wine in hand. It was a tidal surge of extraordinary warmth, and within minutes I'd accepted their invitation to join them for supper.

We went to one of the lacklustre cafes; it was a lot livelier than when I'd passed it earlier, and for a moment we wondered whether they would be able to fit us in. *Sen problema!* said the waiter as he slid two tables together and smoothed paper tablecloths over them, tweaking and re-tweaking as if he were making up some honeymooners' bed with the finest Egyptian cotton sheets. Once seated, it was Estrellas and Albariño on order; discussions of the menu progressed, a change from my staple *pimientos de padrón* and *pulpo a feira*. I decided on *merluza*, and then set about digesting the connections of my newfound friends: four sapphire-eyed sisters, *maybe late forties, early fifties*, Sara, Mary, Patricia, Bernadette; their mother, Fay, *same eyes*; three of their childhood friends, Elizabeth, Cora the brunette, and Abi; Pat (husband of

Mary), Kevin (husband of Elizabeth) and Brendan (married to Abi). Banter pinged up and down the table, scoring roars of belly laughter that turned the heads of the other diners. By the time food arrived I had established from Sara, next to me, that they were all nurses and doctors, that Cora – the other side of me – had come over from Canada for the reunion, and that Fay was an adored matriarch who flicked a whip-quick wit. The fish fell apart in snowy flakes into a garlicky tomato and olive sauce; Cora was regaling me with a bear encounter she had while hiking in the Rockies. We needed to shout to make ourselves heard amid the laughter, and then the table began to erupt from the chimes of plates being struck with knives, a cry of *Don! Don! Don!* went up, Cora joined in; Sara's face flushed, they were hailing a very sunburnt looking man who'd just walked into the restaurant.

'I walked up and down the high street, listening outside all the restaurants, to see which was the noisiest, cos I knew, that's where you reprobates would be,' he said, grin splitting his sore face, and he'd made a beeline for Sara. *Harriet, meet my husband, Don,* she said after he'd kissed her.

Don had started the walk with them, in Sarria. Only he had driven a hire car, *gold would ya believe? A real pimpmobile.* He had cancer and couldn't be exposed to sunlight. They prearranged meetings in cafes on the way; he'd save Fay's legs a couple of kilometres here and there, and then he'd speed ahead to sort accommodation at their destination in time for their arrival. Two days ago he returned home for radiotherapy, and as far as Sara and the rest were concerned, that had been the end of Don's Camino. 'Nah, I couldn't leave them, Harriet,' he said, 'had to get back to them, they'd never manage without me.'

We set off together the next morning at 8 a.m. Don had pin-pointed a cafe on the map where he would meet us for breakfast.

They were walking to the city centre, *Come with us*, they said on hearing I'd be breaking the journey midway, in Lavacolla. It was tempting, to be a part of their happy throng when they hit Santiago, but I wasn't quite ready to finish.

'Your backpack has leaves!' Sara said of the green socks sprouting from my rucksack's straps and pockets.

'I was a bit optimistic with their drying time.'

'I brought ancient clothes ... Don's least favourite of my underwear, I've been chucking them in the bin as we go.'

I laughed. 'Well planned.'

'Feel light as a feather.' She stopped and leant over her poles. 'But good Jaysus, I wasn't expecting this hill ... I thought it'd be downhill all the way now.'

I'd heard rumour of a significant ascent into the municipality of Santiago. We paused to catch our breath and looked back down at the others chatting as they climbed. The cardio workout was tempered by forest and the scent of eucalyptus trees that showered above us, silvery blue. We all walked at different pole-clacking rhythms, and I revelled in the harmony of our percussion and their company.

As Sara and I continued, the tone of our conversation was as easy as it had been the night before, yet there was an added intensity. Amid agreeing it was healthy to feel like an ant in this giant landscape, and chats about her rain-hating beagle and my whippet, she revealed more about Don's illness, his bravery and treatment, and how this uncertainty was impacting their family's life. Every so often she flipped the spotlight to me and I explained that my walk was raising funds for a cancer charity of which the consultant – who saved my life – was a trustee, that I'd wanted a challenge to celebrate the fifth anniversary of my recovery from the angiomyolipoma. We spoke a good deal about life and death.

Don was waiting for us on the stone steps of Casa de Comidas, wearing a white T-shirt emblazoned with Fay's face, and *Fay's Crew* at the top. We piled into the busy bar; the tall figure of Kevin pointed over the crowd to a free table in a corner; we scavenged extra chairs and the laughter began again. Coffee and tortilla arrived and Don wanted to know details of the morning's walk so far; Cora recalled the eagle she saw, *the wingspan on it!* We regaled him with the farmyard where plump white chickens scratched around under a sculpture, and how we'd debated the symbolism of the rusted brown tools and objects dangling from the makeshift crucifix (a saw, old hand drill, pair of scissors, coiled spring, scythe, knife, clamp, buckets, strips of red sweatshirt, paint pot, scallop shell, dustpan brush); *the fabric was Christ's blood, for certain*, Brendan said. *Get on with y'all … It's just a scarecrow*, laughed Bernadette. Second and third coffees were ordered. It was different to being on my own, when I felt compelled not to dally. When we eventually left, Sara called for a group photo on the steps and we huddled in, arms circled round waists and shoulders. Pat snapped away, and then I offered to take pictures with him included. Through the viewfinder, I was dazzled by the pyramid of smiles. A few kilometres later, we parted company after ceremoniously dipping our toes in the stream at Lavacolla and having arranged to meet up in Santiago the following day. I waved them off and we shouted a final *Buen Camino!* The four sisters took the lead and they disappeared down the road, poles clacking. As I headed back to the village centre, it felt as if I'd taken off a jacket fit for the Antarctic, such was the sudden draught of my own company.

I first learnt about the Camino from a young Spanish magician practising his tricks on a Waterloo-bound train. Our fellow passengers had remained riveted to their devices but I couldn't help commenting, and so we got into conversation while he shuffled his pack of cards as if he was playing the concertina. *There's only one way to get to know Spain,* he said, *and that's to walk the Camino.* He disappeared into the crowd of commuters at Waterloo a bit like the disappearing gold coin that had first brought me to his attention; *Buen Camino!* he called after me. Seven months later, the magic began again at the starting point of my walk, O'Cebreiro – the tiny pre-Roman village perched at 1,300m – where I was introduced to the spectacle of Galician fog. Setting off the first morning was disconcerting, I could see nothing behind me – as if the past had been erased, and the way ahead was unclear, so much so that my walking pole prodded the ground in front, midst churning whiteness, to check that I wasn't about to fall off the mountainside. The stage curtain gradually lifted, revealing glimpses of shadowy, undulating horizon. As each layer of mist dissolved, hues of blue, green and brown brought the mountainside into focus – the view catapulted me to a standstill, nothing had prepared me for such soul-jolting beauty. Every day I was treated to the fog's reveal, and when the walk was over, one of the things I missed most was the thrill of those hidden mornings.

When researching the Camino, I learnt that – as *pilgrimage* suggests – the Camino used to be just Christians walking to the cathedral in Santiago de Compostela, where they believed St James to be buried; nowadays the route is popular with all faiths and non-believers, and I wondered what it was about the journey that remained so compelling. After a day or two of walking, I noticed it was more common to see *peregrinos* walking in pairs or groups; solo hikers were a minority, and the etiquette of wishing everyone you passed a cheery *Buen Camino!* made it a more inclusive experience. Even locals and passing cyclists and motorists would call out the greeting. By the time I met Fay's Crew I had walked 150km alone, save for the few occasions I'd fallen into step with other *peregrinos*. I discovered there was no such thing as small talk on the Camino. Possibly because the question everyone seemed to ask within minutes of meeting is, *What made you walk the Camino?* And because everybody has a story, and time together is but a few kilometres, the answer cuts the small talk. The little shrines that dotted the way, where faces, some young, and some old, would smile at you heartbreakingly from photos positioned in the hollow of a tree were a poignant reminder that many stories were about loss.

I walked a while with Henrik, who had hiked the first two weeks with his wife before she returned home, as planned, to their children in Germany, leaving him to complete the second half of the journey. I recognised him from an earlier point on the route; he was a noticeable figure as he wore a harness that pulled a cart-like contraption he had designed himself, loaded with his backpack and camping equipment. Henrik told me his story, that he had been a dependable, successful businessman when shortly after his mother died he became bedridden with depression. Used to travelling the world, he was suddenly terrified to go anywhere alone. He even had to learn to drive alone again. Walking the Camino in its 790km entirety marked the end of this two-year struggle with the illness. *It's proof that I'm literally on the road again … that I'm now in a position to choose solitude rather than allow it to inhabit me.* I confessed that although my official reason for walking was to celebrate my recovery and to raise funds for the Mulberry Centre, the subtext was that the Camino was providing me with focus. I was having trouble pulling myself together following the end of my engagement. I felt guilty generally that I hadn't fashioned a success story with the gift of recovery … It seemed that all I had subsequently achieved was a failed relationship (that contained a failed pregnancy, and with it my chance of motherhood). I needed to come to terms with absence, and thought perhaps I could literally walk out of the funk. The intimacy with which Henrik and I spoke in those three hours of walking was an interaction I shall forever treasure.

Henrik said that there had been more *stuff* attached to his cart, like pots and pans that he hadn't needed and had given away, *lightening my load*, as he went along. Pretty much everything about walking the Camino (and possibly pilgrimages in general) lends itself to metaphor, from the word *camino*[89] itself to fog to backpacks and blisters; it's a microcosm of life complete with ups and downs. As well as the shrines, the piles of wayside stones snagged my heart. It was a pilgrim ritual to find a stone, and walk with it in their hand, aware of its weight, its roughness or smoothness, put their sorrow into it, and to leave it on one of the mounds, to unburden themselves.

Looking back at my Camino photographs, they are primarily of sublime landscapes, some punctuated with cows, or abandoned dwellings, others veiled with fog. Apart from incidental captures, there are only five of people – portraits of the *peregrinos* that I walked with and whose conversations, like Henrik's, often fly round my mind. The fifth picture, of Fay's Crew, still astounds me. Their smiles and whole beings shine. It reminds me of the serendipity of our encounter; its timing, a final abracadabra. I still cannot believe how fortunate I was to meet them. After walking the Camino, it occurred to me that, although we use images of place to describe illness and pain, it is in place that we seek solace for pain. Landscape allows us to get away from it all but to be with it all. The walking, dwelling and noticing affords us time to reflect upon it. Fay's Crew epitomised the Camino. Unsaid, they were, of course, walking as much for Don (and Sara) as they were for Fay. In celebration of both their wonderful lives.

---

89   Camino means path in Spanish, but the greeting *Buen Camino* in its *go well* sentiment refers to the more spiritual path of life's journey.

We found each other, as arranged, under the swing and smoke of the Botafumeiro at the midday Pilgrim's Mass, shortly after I'd walked into Santiago de Compostela. We spent the afternoon together, queuing at the pilgrims' office to present our stamped *credencials* in return for *compostelas*, eating tapas and exploring the old town. I hadn't wanted to gate-crash their evening but they were insistent I join them, *and this evening's my treat,* Fay had said firmly. Don caught Kevin unawares halfway through the meal with a cheque on behalf of the crew in gratitude for his planning of their Camino; the money was to replace his bicycle that had been stolen. Cue speeches from both men that were in turn hilarious and moving, provoking more raucous laughter, banging of the table, and tears. Don made several other impromptu and humorous awards, and even remembered me: I was awarded a miniature leprechaun *peregrino* for being 'best friend made on the Camino'. They flew back to Ireland the following morning, and I caught the bus to Finisterre. The leprechaun has remained on my desk, not far from my hospital memento, the candleholder given to me by Mrs Mohammed.

Buen Camino

Chapter Twenty-One

The traffic inches along Fulham Palace Road.

'Feeling okay?' asks Emily from the back.

'Perfect,' I say.

'Comfortable?'

'I really am fine.'

Looking out of the window, I feel like I've downed more of Alice in Wonderland's draught. *I am actually down here* – a dot in that view from the bathroom – everything and everyone is towering.

Lives: young, old, middling.

Rushing. Dawdling. Drifting.

Crowded shopfronts. Weaving cyclists.

A slam of a parked car door, horns, sirens.

Laughing down phone; drag of cigarette; newspaper tucked under arm. Worn expressions; *must push on*. Animated faces; chat stops. Hand in hand. Scudding litter. Kids in buggies, podgy fingers and crisp packet. Street corner kiss. Bus queues; carriers straining with weekend groceries. Colour. Lights. Fluorescent. Hammersmith Bridge groans. Scullers out on river. Life.

*

We park. The un-clunk of Emily's seat belt, and she's out of the car in a jiffy, opening my door.

'Take your time,' she says. One foot meets grainy tarmac ...

Pause: It's cold and rainy outside and I feel the gravelly road score my bare feet.

Play: A neighbour's tawny tabby saunters past. A plane overhead. I look up and down the terrace of Victorian cottages. No one's around. Everything is the same, as if I'd just nipped out for a pint of milk. The trees have more leaves; that is all.

Through the small wooden gate.

The front door opens.

'You're here,' says my mother, her arms go round me and I feel the softness of her navy-jumpered shoulder on my chin.

'Yes,' I say, 'I'm here.' Aromas – this morning's coffee, toast, washing powder, polish, perfume – come together and configure, like a PIN number, into the smell of home. I swallow hard. The feeling deep in my chest that I couldn't define as we left Charing Cross is taking form.

'Come on through,' she guides me into the sitting room. 'I've moved the sofa round.'

I gravitate to its new corner by the bay window. 'Let me arrange the pillows,' and she jigsaws them as they were in hospital.

'It's nice, the sofa here.'

'I had the carpets and furniture steam-cleaned yesterday ...'

'Really?'

'I wanted everywhere germ free. While they were moving things around I thought you might be snugger if it were this way round. Now, what can I get you?'

'Nothing, nothing at all. I'm happy. To be home.'

Her love sonar ripples round my heart; it aches.

'Where's Harvey?'

'I knew you'd be disappointed. He'll be home tomorrow, after you've had a chance to settle.'

We have tea. *Builders.* The mugs are decades old; in my cannula-pitted hands, their familiarity is precious and rare as if the mugs have been borrowed from a museum display case, relics from the very scenes of ancient pastoral Japan their faded designs depict. It tastes different to hospital tea.

I sit. Alone. Peace. *Tranquillity has its own acoustics.* Close my eyes: there's a domed roof, mosaicked with gold-leaf. Birdsong from the street: each chirrup turns tiles to turquoise and emerald. The creaks of floorboards upstairs are squares of ruby and claret. The sound of chopping from the kitchen: blade-silver. A pattern spreads ivily across the golden dome, its brilliance reflecting the echoes, as if I'm hearing these sounds for the very first time. Open my eyes: they are smarting again. The birdsong chirps on. I stand up. And walk, arms stuck out at the sides, to the stairs.

Pause: One step at a time, to the bathroom; the stitch is tightening.

Play: One hand on the banister, I'm upstairs relatively quickly. I push the door open.

Pause: The bathroom floor has stretched: it's expansive, the corners have been yanked out; its grey has become the whitest sheet ...

Play: The room is as compact as ever. I clock its new additions. There's a bench over the bath, and a grab handle above it on the tiled wall. The loo seat really is throne-like with the raised contraption. I cannot look at the floor. I wash my hands – fig-scented soap – and then I catch sight of the stranger. I cannot look at the mirror either.

Down the stairs. Hand on banister, carpet melts into each barefoot step. Eyes on front door. Into the kitchen.

'What are you doing up?'

'I *have* been up. The bathroom's very well ... um, um, set up isn't it?' *Can't think of the word.*

'You've been up the stairs? Without me keeping an eye out?' She's put down the knife next to a pile of carrot batons.

'I have to go up alone sometime.'

'Perhaps just not the first few times.' She resumes her slicing.

'This is nice,' I say, easing into the tall white chair, next to the garden door.

The cat flap flips open. For a moment it is just Columbus's grey owlish face that's visible, as he looks me up and down with unblinking green eyes. Simon always says that Columbus reminds him of toothpaste being squeezed out of a tube, the way he struggles his bulk through the flap. *Maine Coons are supposed to be big*, my mother says with emphatic patience should Ian, our vet, make any tentative suggestion that her beloved could do with shedding a few pounds. *It's fur, that's all it is.*

'Hey Clumpypaws, how are you?' I ask the yowling fluffy cloud as he weaves in and out of my mother's feet.

'Hungry aren't you, Blossom?' and my mother reaches for his food bowl.

This vignette of simple domesticity is varnished with the exotica of a Henri Rousseau scene where Columbus is a peeping tiger and all the kitchen utensils are huge and colourful jungle plants, and my mother chopping is a woman playing a xylophone. I head back to the sitting room and to the little corner spot, yawning so deeply that my jaw does the splits.

Just before Emily left she had taken Mr Winkler's discharge letter from her handbag and put the envelope on the sofa next to me. It's still there. I open it automatically, too quickly.

'... *This young lady was admitted on 10th March. She presented with a giant angiomyolipoma of the right kidney. This had continually ruptured and she presented with a catastrophic retroperitoneal haemorrhage and an incredibly large haematoma. Her Hb was 4. She was resuscitated at the West Middlesex Hospital and transferred with blue light to Charing Cross Hospital. Here she had an emergency embolisation of the feeding vessel to the ruptured and bleeding angiomyolipoma. After this, the large retroperitoneal mass and haematoma were treated conservatively. She required considerable nutritional and analgesic support. Gradually her symptoms improved. Currently she is on OxyNorm and Amitriptyline for pain control. She is mobilising well but is still considerably incapacitated. Her main problem is positional pain in the upper and lower back related to compression of nerves and other intra-abdominal cavities. This I would expect to continue for some time. The aim of her management is to let the retroperitoneal haematoma resolve over the next 3–6 months and then reappraise the situation. She may need an open radical nephrectomy in the future ...'*

Young is good. He definitely has a charming side, Mr Winkler. *Catastrophic* and *resuscitated* waltz in letters as huge and bold like the top row of an eye test. Natural disasters that cause massive life loss and wipe out villages are described as catastrophic; as for *resuscitated* ... surely it belongs safe and sound in hospital soaps.

'Apparently I may need a nephrectomy?' I say to my mother.

'Yes, Mr Winkler mentioned some time ago that you have to have your kidney removed,' she says, watching my face.

Open radical nephrectomy ...

Pause: 'We're going to have to remove your kidney,' Jessica Worth, Anaesthetist at West Middlesex Hospital.

Play: 'And it says here that I was resuscitated?'

'Yes. You were.' Fear speckles my mother's eyes. 'May I have a look?'

I hand her the letter and she reads it, giving the occasional nod. 'You were really poorly. It must be frightening, reading it in black and white like this?'

'Resuscitated though?' I still cannot get my head round it.

*

At 9.30 p.m. I'm ready for bed. In my room there's a faint smell of paint, bookshelves have been put up and there's a new chest of drawers.

'Wow.'

'Do you like it? Got rid of all the clutter! Chris did the shelving. He hardly charged anything … considering the time he took, and the workmanship,' my mother says, switching on the bedside light. Chris is our next-door neighbour.

'They're brilliant. Thank you. For making everything so perfect and easy.'

'No need to thank me. I just want you to be as comfortable as possible,' she says, half out of the door and turning off the main light. 'I'll be up in a few minutes with your tablets.'

As I pull off garments, the lamp casts my shadowy staccato movements across the wall. I put on the night things that she's left out for me and sit on the edge of the bed, now fitted with rails. This is what I've been imagining since HDU. There's a heap of pillows, I push all but two to one side and lie back. The feeling of bliss that I've envisaged for weeks does not happen. Instead, my stomach and right side yelp with the stretch. I try and sit up, and manage to get up on my elbows, for seconds only. Back flat. My heart starts racing. I'm stuck. *Stop panicking. Deep breath.* I twist, grab on to the rails and drag myself up. *Damn. I still need the pillows then.* I kick the duvet down so that I can pull it over me. The duvet. It settles: warm, weightless. I sigh, and slide my legs around in the field of space.

'How are you getting on?' My mother pops her head round the door with an enquiring smile.

'Oh my word. Heaven.'

'I can believe it,' she says, putting down a tray with fizzy water and tablets on the desk next to my bed. 'Here, let me give you a hand with your pillows.'

I lean back and now bliss takes a grip.

*

I wake up coughing and reach for some tissues. It's dark; the over-bed table is not there. Instead, poking out from under the duvet, are four substantial spider legs. My entire being leaps; I scramble for the lamp switch. And peer. No tarantula, but a flamenco fan of creases in the sheet. No over-bed table because *You're home, silly.* I look at my phone and it's 3 a.m.

Pause: There's a stitch tearing down my right side.

Play: I turn the lamp off and push the pillows back into a triangular wedge. For a while I'm content tracing the outline of the wardrobe, until its engrained eyes stare back at me, and the crack that runs across the ceiling deepens. Things appear friendlier with the lamp switched on again. Now it's my SLR camera that stares down from the new shelves, like Cyclops with a grin. Chris has done a really smart job: I scan the books, their titles wailing to be put in some kind of order, and smile when I spot Little Leopard-Faced Orchid's flowers tickling the spine of *Tess of the D'Urbervilles. We're home.* Sleepy again. Close my eyes. Bricks. Not red, crumbling ones. They're paler. My father's mixing cement – he's building a pond.

Each morning at 7 a.m., my mother brings OxyNorm, tea and fruit salad – apple, bananas, kiwi, blueberries, pineapple and chopped dates and almonds, dewy with juice. The first couple of days, a navy-uniformed nurse visits early to take blood and to check that I am managing to get up. No need. I find my routine. Simple actions like getting out of bed are still time-warped, but by 10.30 a.m. I'm ensconced on the sofa. The trick, I have discovered, is not to go anywhere without the Grabber and the cloth bag that contains essentials. I make a pact with myself that there will be no daytime TV during this recovery period. The noticeable improvement is concentration; in the stillness of the sitting room I have begun to read again. And so days dissolve, reading and dozing interspersed with snacks and short bouts of exercise. Harvey is my shadow. He is curled up next to me on the sofa, or waiting outside the bathroom door, or with my mother at the front gate as every day I progress two houses further along the road, trying to keep my arms closer to my sides and less penguin-like. The aim remains: to walk in Bushy Park, as soon as possible.

*

Sitting on the shower bench. Apart from my feet, which have regained their birth smoothness, I'm scalier than a snake. My skin is moulting. I rub away with a flannel to find the new me. It takes days.

And I'm a freak show; my naked stomach continues to bulge grotesquely, protruding from the scrawny rest of me. It's *as if the gargoyles have actually taken residence in my belly*. On weighing myself I discover that I have lost over two stone.

I finally get to wash my hair during the second week of being home. As my fingertips work my scalp, lather mountain-streams down the weird rest of me. My arms ache, there's a lot of hair to rinse and untangle. Dark inkblots float in and out of vision. The hairdryer weighs a ton.

Independence, though, is glucose, the energy it inspires.

*

'May I examine your tummy? I'll be careful not to hurt you.' An unscheduled home visit from GP Dr Christy. Steely grey, urchin-cropped hair with a youthful face.

'Of course.'

'How could we have let this happen?' She looks up from her gentle probing of my right side.

'How could you have known?' I ask. How could they, if I hadn't even recognised there had been something wrong.

*

It is increasingly apparent that I've misplaced words, perhaps half of my vocabulary. That feeling, of a word being on the tip of your tongue but beyond the realm of recall, is ever present. Conversations are sticky and stuttering. It's not just vocabulary. I browse the shelves of read books in my mind; choose a title only to find blank pages. The same with films. It's as if someone has broken into my library and robbed me of every plot.

'I'm sure it's just the drugs. As you stop taking them, your memory will improve. You'll see!' Dr Christy had reassured me.

This frustration fuels a renewed, unquenchable thirst for reading. The last time I read in such quantity – for pleasure – must have been at boarding school. It was the best medication for homesickness. The first book that nine-year-old me selected from the school library was Ian Serraillier's *The Silver Sword*. Tucked behind the floor-to-ceiling curtains of the Junior Common Room – where I usually snuck to watch the berry lights of Miss Rogers's moped zoom into the night before the dormitory call to bed – I was at once in Nazi-invaded Warsaw. Quite coincidentally, the next book I picked was *The Diary of Anne Frank*. My homesickness really didn't seem so bad. Around that time, Grandma ignited my veterinary dreams when she introduced me to James Herriot, and then to Gerald Durrell and other true stories with an animal focus. One left an indelible impression: Sheila Hocken's *Emma and I* recounted her relationship with her guide dog, and how she subsequently – and miraculously – regained her eyesight. Hocken's transition and recalibration, from darkness to the visual world – the synergy of shadowy shapes meeting their detailed, technicoloured counterparts: long-known voices to faces; a scentless flower to a vibrant dahlia; hands to veiny ugliness; grass to blades of numerous greens – particularly affected me. It was like watching twins separated at birth being reunited years on.

In between these memoirs, and in the school holidays, I got hooked on mysteries:

Nom is having a break from her weeding. We're on the swing-seat. *Gently does it, girls,* she says, puffing at her Lambert and Butler; we've swung into a rhythm: canopy – blue sky – canopy – blue sky – creak – giggle – creak – giggle – creak. That's enough now, *I can't concentrate on my book,* giggle – creak – giggle – creak, *you don't want me to fetch your father now, do you?* There's an edge to her voice that slows our kicking legs and we get on with chain-chewing Opal Fruits. *Anyway, I'm going to go and find Daddy,* Emily says, sliding off. *More room for us, anyway!* I call after my sister, watching her sturdy little legs stomp up the garden steps. Nom's finished her cigarette and I cosy up to her and start reading the extra-large print of her cellophane-covered library book, *Cards on the Table,* that she's balancing on her chest. Someone called Poirot is talking to someone called Ariadne. *Who's Poyrot, is he a pirate?* I ask. *It's pronounced Pworo, he's a Belgian detective,* Nom says, stroking my hair, her eyes not leaving the print. When she dozes off I carry on reading. On our next visit to Langport library I join Nom in the adult section and take out *Crooked House.*

It's during the same holiday that I run my finger along all the authors on my father's orange-spined, penguin-dotted shelves. He must like D.H. Lawrence because he has about ten of his books. And Chekhov ... that must be why he sometimes says things are ChekOFFian. But, the BIG mystery is that I hardly ever see him read a book. Only a newspaper. On Sundays.

We're sitting round the dining room table having lunch.

'What's your favourite book, Daddy?' I ask.

'I've never read much. Not the best question for a dyslexic.'

'Mummy says I might be dysLEXic,' says Emily, pointing at herself with her spoon.

'I wouldn't be surprised. You're lucky ... it wasn't recognised in my day,' he says with a bloodshot glare at Nom. And a glug of cider from his tankard.

'Delicious soup, Christopher,' says Nom.

'But, Daddy ...'

'Yes, Harriet.'

'Whose books are they on your bookshelves?'

'They belong to me.'

'I'm a *smidgen* confused.'

I'm hoping for a smile; he doesn't notice that I've dipped into his candy jar of words.

'Why so?'

'Have you read them?'

'Of course I've read them, every one.'

'Did you wake up one day and decide not to read anymore?'

'What *is* this, the Spanish Inquisition?'

'You said that you've never read much.'

289

'Exactly. *Much*. Think about it.'

'Um ...'

'It's all to do with relativism, isn't it? The Sophists. Wasn't it? How we measure our quantities of much, and by what criteria.'

'Oh, Christopher! She's only a child.'

'Does that mean I have to ply my daughter's inquiring mind with saccharine, Mother? Talk to my children as if they're blancmange, and not challenge thought?'

My father's cheeks are reddening.

'A relaxing lunch would be nice.' Our grandmother sighs.

'My favourite is *Wilberforce the Whale*.' Emily says this as if it is a full stop to the whole conversation and drowns a slice of bread in her bowl of soup.

'I wouldn't interfere if I were you, Mother. If you and Father had been more observant, I might've left school with decent qualifications.'

'Name just one book you liked, there must have been one, Daddy.'

One last try.

'Very well. *White Fang*. By Jack London. I remember enjoying that very much, and *Lorna Doone*. Have you read either of them?'

'Not yet, Daddy.'

From my corner spot on the sofa, with Philip Kerr's *Berlin Noir* trilogy hefty on my lap, I picture myself back at Rookesbury, waiting for the post, looking out for the brown manila envelopes with my mother's italic handwriting that contained maybe an Agatha Christie or a Dick Francis and a whisper of *Mitsouko*. And I ponder the mystery of how, in spite of his claims of undiagnosed dyslexia, my thirteen-year-old father's reading choices were far more sophisticated than my own at boarding school, of how nascent intent nested within them:

'Springfield'
Wycliffe College,
Lampeter,
Cardiganshire,
Wales
21st March, 1944

Dear Daddy,

... In an English essay last week I had to write on the subject 'what I should like to be'. The heading I contrived was 'My Ambitions'. I said I should like to take a degree in Veterinary Surgeonship (I hope that's what one calls it). Then to go abroad and mix with the wild, to get as close to them as possible and lead a regular Tarzany or 'wild man o' the woods' life and after a long period return to 'civilisation' and write an account of my adventures. I might possibly change my mind. I do not know.

As to being a journalist, the idea seems very attractive to me. My English teacher says I have a flair for writing but as you say I have to learn to SPELL properley. (sic) I'm having an onward battle to see what literature I should read. On one side Conan Doyle novels beckon, on the other classics. I am doing 50% of each.

The finest books I have ever read I think are *Lorna Doone* and *Tom Brown's Schooldays*. In the latter I have come across one or too (sic) points which I myself have experienced. In *Lorna Doone* I admire the superfine descriptions of the country, men and animals, which believe me are exquisite.

As to school work I came fourth out of twelve but seem to lack the power of concentration. Mr Sibly says that I ought to be in a form higher. But I can't concentrate. I am getting on well in a lesson when I start thinking about something else. I try to drive it way out of my mind when my vivid imagination enlarges on it. Please would you give me some advice?

With much love,
from your very
affectionate son,
Christopher xxx

It's Simon who's supplying me now with my fixes of Kerr and Second World War fiction, and thrillers generally – from Robert Harris to Henning Mankell – genres that have not been on my reading horizon since those Rookesbury days.

There are interludes, though.

Thought you might like this, the woman in the bookshop raved about it, says Finlay, handing me Tony Harrison's *Collected Poems* and then settling in the armchair opposite as if he had seen me just last week. He doesn't make any comment about my appearance nor ask me too many questions. He just talks about his work and music. And I sit back and listen.

*

There was a clatter of cattle grid when we entered Bushy Park, on this first post-hospital visit. My mother drove up Chestnut Avenue, the Christopher Wren-designed tree-lined approach to Hampton Court, keeping precisely to the 20mph speed limit while I knocked back shot upon shot of green.

A lulling breeze.

It's warm, even for mid-May. Bushy Park has literal benchmarks. I'm on the bench nearest the car park, the one that has given me many a weekend snigger, *Look at them! Picnicking there! Exhaust surf lapping at their toes!* Monday, today; only five other cars. I've been sitting here a few minutes and my back is already grumbling; I snigger at myself, *See, karma for such sneering.*

An arrow of parakeets shriek as one, in a fly-past.

I breathe in the sweat of the park – the dankness of long grass, the musky odour of deer.

Before my mother set off, we'd scanned the horizon for stag antlers, rising above ferns like shark fins. I gave her the all-clear, and now she follows Harvey, her gait a little stiff, along trodden down and tufted paths as he bounces through bracken, part kangaroo, part meerkat. Every so often she turns to wave at me. When we rescued him, he was a year old and called Blaze because of the white flash on his muzzle; *Not terribly imaginative,* said my mother, and she renamed him Harvey after the James Stewart movie. He was meant to be her dog: the thought was that whippets make good company, that when you take them out they pretty much exercise themselves – wouldn't be a burden on her arthritis. All true of the pocket-rocket. Inevitably, I exercised him most, and as much as he loves my mother, it is to me he limpeted his gentle soul. The day after he arrived, I brought him to the park and he shivered on the back seat of the Morris Minor, in time with the engine's vibrations. Amongst these ferns, on an August scorcher, he levitated several feet off the ground when the wings of a Red Admiral brushed his shoulder. No such skittishness today. He's off. It must be a rabbit. He's changed direction and now he's just running for the hell of it, galloping ever-increasing laps. My mother stops to watch. And it *is* pure *joie de vivre*: the effortlessness of his racehorse stride, the uncomplicated loveliness of it. Like Alice and Maddy's laughter.

I walk – my hands still straying out to the sides – a couple of metres over to a bleached-out lightning tree. I lean against it, barkless as driftwood, and kick off my Birkenstocks. The grass is cool, damp; blades poke between toes, evergreen trees above my snowy feet. *I am here.*

*

I'm denting local supplies of black grapes, spinach and dried apricots, foods suggested to counter the blots that float in front of my eyes, a symptom of anaemia. Although my appetite is improving, since I got home I've become obsessive about not consuming any fat. I marvel at my jutting, cubist ribs, they compensate for the swell of gargoyle. This is not something I share with anyone.

*

I'm standing in my bedroom doorway. It's 3 a.m., again. My heart is beating way out of its comfort zone; beads of perspiration prickle my forehead. I've been awake for about an hour convinced that the crack in the ceiling is widening, that I am about to be buried by the entire contents of the loft, parcel-taped boxes from all stages of our lives, including my father's massive vinyl collection. I snap on the light and immediately feel foolish. There *is* a whole house of stuff in the loft, and there *is* a bulge; it's more of a seam that runs across the width of the ceiling, paint splitting into a short hairline crack at the middle point, not far from the light fitting. The crack is no wider.

*

Emily and I are in the kitchen. I'm perched on the white chair. She's decided to have a clear-out as a surprise for our mother – who returned to work today – and has already emptied the larder cupboard.

'So, how did it go, yesterday?'

'All absolutely fine, I told you so on the phone.'

'Come on. I need details! How was my favourite doctor?' She squints at the lid of a jar of chutney, and puts it to one side. Obviously past its sell-by date. My sister's silvery tone doesn't entirely disguise apprehension in her register. 'He seemed pleased to see me.' *Remarkable progress, Harriet,* he'd said, showing us into his consulting room, having watched me walk towards him, and shaken our hands under the beam of his smile.

'Of course he was. What's the angiomyolipoma up to?' Another jar joins the chutney.

'No change, all fine. He showed us the scans on his computer, the previous ones, and how the kidney looks in comparison to the left one. It's like watching footage of some outer space planet. Apparently they're discussing it, what should be done, at their interdisciplinary meetings. Funny, that.'

'Funny that a team of consultants should be sitting round a table, discussing little old you?'

'Exactly. Less of the old, you.' We both laugh. I give her the thumbs-up as she gestures towards jars and dried ingredients now squarely regimented on the shelves.

'But everything's okay?'

'Yup. He said it's stable, that we must watch and wait.'

'He has to be cautious, to cover himself.' She's moved on to crockery.

'I know. I'm getting used to it … Oh, I mentioned the memory problems.'

'And?'

'He wasn't particularly interested, said that I'd see an improvement when I eventually come off the meds.'

'Well, go with that then.'

'So, I asked if I could start cutting down the OxyNorm, and he agreed.'

'That's great. What about exercise?'

'Continue with *gentle* walking but nothing with impact, *no jogging* – as if I could – the best thing would be swimming … And I asked when I could drive.'

Emily laughs, knowing that my impatience to get back behind the wheel of my Morris Minor is a source of contention. 'Oh yes?'

'Not for another six weeks.'

'Bummer.'

'Mmm.' I watch my sister's ponytail swish as she finishes wiping the insides of the bare cupboard.

'And how was Moms yesterday?'

'Fantastic as ever. She asked the questions I'd forgotten, which was probably over half of them. And ones which hadn't occurred to me.'

'Did you pop into the ward?'

'We didn't go to Charing Cross, we saw him at West Middlesex.'

'I'll be glad to never see that hospital again.' She looks at me over her shoulder.

'It was sweltering in his consulting room.'

Chinks of work surface blink between the varyingly stacked piles of dishes.

'You know, when I arrived there that night, a nurse took me into a little room. She told me to *prepare for the worst*.' Her head's back in the cupboard and her voice is tinny.

Emily starts putting the crockery that's not used every day back onto the higher shelves; she still has her back to me.

'I went to get a coffee. Put money in the machine. It was in one of those little plastic cups, nothing to them. My hand was shaking so much that I dropped it … the coffee spilt over my hand, scalded me. I didn't feel it at all …'

The lower shelves now. Mugs, cups, everyday plates. She's paused. Her shoulders are slightly hunched. That I've caused them this level of fear and worry is huge to assimilate; the guilt is strangling. I slide off the white chair and go over to put the kettle on. I sense Emily doesn't want to be touched, hugged.

*

I'm sleeping a lot.

On the sofa: I nod off every couple of chapters. Sometimes a twenty-minute nap, sometimes an hour or two. It's the cosy kind of sleep that comes in like the tide, after eating too much at Christmas; when rain streams down the windows, absolving any thought of a walk, and there is nothing to be done other than drift. Where waking up is velvety, eyes still closed; listening out for the rain, murmurs of conversation as they lap against the shore of consciousness.

In bed: sleep is dreamful, intense and fractured, patrolled by Vigilance flashing a torch into my eyes, several times a night. To check. That everything is okay. That I'm here. At weekends, I stir to music coming from Chris and Emma's garden. Snatches of discussion and laughter waft through my open window, on spirals of grass, its smoke evoking long-ago Lampeter nights. I start recognising voices from these into-dawn parties, and imagine their faces; I trace relationships by untangling spools of their chat. They beckon, as if I am one of them, and I tag along, up a hill, moon on the horizon. Then we're in a grand house. Pillars and blood-red sofas in every room. Mingling with doctors and nurses. Quaffing cocktails.

All this sleep does not preclude attacks of super-tiredness. They strike with urgency, like raw thirst. There's no argument; I have to lie down. Flat. These attacks usually occur after the exertion of an outing. Apart from the park, there have been journeys to the physio, to the GP for blood tests, and one day I popped into the bank. My mother had pulled up a few shops down. *Shall I come with you?* she'd offered. Out of the car, I'd walked purposefully to Lloyds, aware of my penguin-ness, and noticing every crevice and cigarette butt of the pavement. In the bank I queued to pay in a cheque. I soaked up the extraordinariness of doing this mundane thing. It was like being in a bank of a foreign country. The cashier said, *Next, please,* and then there I was handing over the cheque, watching her fuchsia lips as if I was going to catch them not syncing with her chitchat. *There, that's all paid in for you. Anything more I can help you with today, Miss Mercer?* I wondered whether she assumed I was pregnant, whether I looked as touristy as I felt.

Mr Winkler said six months of recuperation. The plan is to be back at work before then. I decide it's time to learn to swim properly. I'm coughing and spluttering.

'Did you have your eyes open or closed?' asks Donna, the instructor, who is poolside.

'Closed.'

'That's the problem. Closed eyes underwater disorientates the brain. Try again, with your eyes open.'

I take a deep breath, submerge, and open my eyes to the side of the pool; I look down past my haematoma-bump – sculpted by the black swimsuit – and glimpse my toes, and then resurface without panic.

'Better? … Now this time, blow bubbles while you are under.'

Thanks to Donna's clear instruction and a pair of goggles, I am swimming head-dipping breaststroke after a couple of sessions. The stroke repetition is addictive and hypnotic, like a form of

GARGOYLES

meditation. I love the fleeting immersion, the blue and womblike underwater world, where a second stops still.

The swimming gives me confidence; although it shocks me, still, to meet the gaze of my reflection in the bathroom mirror. I sense that it's going to take more than walking, swimming and reading to find my way back to the page I left in March. I want to see friends, and I'm more than thankful for their thoughts, but there's a part of me that's self-conscious about my touristy self, and the stuttering word loss. *They'll definitely notice.* My strangeness and vocabulary holes are not so glaring with family, and I include Max, Melody, Tania and Finlay in this bracket. The others, though? Not yet. I'm protective of the cocoon of home.

*

Paved Court is striped with shadows; lobelia, pansies, begonias and geraniums spill their blossom over the window boxes above each shop. I ring the brass bell on the black-gloss painted doorframe. Through the glass I see the mourning table, the conservatory out at the back, and then Susan comes into view, surprise and a smile lighting her face as she approaches the door. She will have been sitting at the desk and seen us on the CCTV. Inside, standing on the softness of rug, I'm drunk on the familiar scent of Aqua di Palma room fragrance and wood polish.

... You should've told us you were coming ... Oh it was very last minute ... What can I get you both, coffee? Water? ...

A few steps round to the 'office'.

'You don't look as bad as I thought you'd look,' Nye says (*that phrase, again*) with a massive grin, he gets up from the desk and opened stock-books, and hugs me. There were moments in hospital, particularly on the observation ward, when I missed our conversations and retraced their breadth. His texts were among those from friends that I was sad to lose during the Harry Potter and the Missing Phone debacle. Afterwards, when we leave Susan's, I feel that the visit has propelled me forwards. I celebrate by choosing some new perfume. Since I've been home I haven't been able to tolerate the scent of the perfume that I've worn for years.

*

It's mid-June. We've parked in the street, entered Bushy Park on foot, through the wrought-iron gates of the Blandford Road pedestrian entrance. This is the entrance that Harvey and I would normally walk to from home; it takes about ten minutes give-or-take, depending on the extent of the day's canine gossip columns to be read at lampposts. Today's the day that I get to go off-piste. Alone. Well, almost. Until now we've stuck to the more central area of the park, where I've progressed to the next bench on each visit. No benches today.

'So, I'll walk parallel and follow the wall until you stop,' says my mother, nodding towards the red-brick wall running the perimeter of the park.

'Let's aim for the cricket pitch ... sit for a bit ... watch the world.'

'Lovely idea. Got your phone?'

'Right here.' I pat my little woven shoulder bag.

'Don't go too quickly, will you? Take your time.'

'Please stop worrying,' I say, and follow Harvey off into waves of fern and grass.

The sky is lapis, the greenery lush; the whippet is kangarooing ahead. *People really will think you're a loony if you don't lower the volume on that smile*, I tell myself. Our back garden, though, seems happily free of other walkers. Harvey's leading me through ticklish long grass; the blades whispering against my milk-bottle calves. *Wow, the sun's warm on my shoulders.* Harvey's sniffing some undergrowth with suspicious intent; he'd better not roll. Fox poo is his rub of choice. This has to be the first time I've worn a dress to the park. Probably the first time I've worn a dress voluntarily since ... forever. In the last weeks, I've laughed at myself spending ridiculous amounts of time online exploring styles and fabrics that might accommodate the bulge of alien, before finally hitting my credit card with two of them. Today I'm wearing the indigo floral number; it has a 1950s vibe. Good, Harvey's moved on. I look across to the wall and realise how far out we've roamed, as if I'm a swimmer suddenly struck by how distant the shore has become. My mother's waving figure is tiny. I wave back. I'm feeling good.

The shouts are muffled, and I pay them no more attention than mild irritation at their intrusion of my idyll. I look behind and see a woman. She's running. A jogger. I carry on. The shouts get closer, and clearer. I hear fear, and an American accent, 'HELP! HELP!' I was wrong. She's not running for fun. *Uh oh.* She's being pursued by a stag and three, maybe four deer. It's a slo-mo couple of seconds before the penny drops; my mother's wave was far from the casual gesture I'd assumed. They've passed the woman and are heading in my direction. The lightness of their stride; antlers like branches, cutting the air.

I remember having read somewhere that it's better to leave dogs off the lead in this situation. *C'mon Harvey.* I start to run. *Yes, gentle walking is fine.* And *Perhaps even try some swimming.* More walkers on the horizon now. Run. Run. *But absolutely nothing with impact, jogging for example is out of the question.* Mr Winkler's laser eyes. I hear my phone ringing. Keep going. My heart rate's accelerated off the clock.

Panting, out of breath. Shades falling down my nose. Push them back up. *No impact. No impact,* I repeat to myself with every stride. *Ha ha ha* … Hospital beds flash before me. Two months ago I couldn't commute 30cm from bed to chair. I'm running and stumbling, inhaling all the green I could possibly want, Harvey at my side. Heart's pounding at the V of my dress, like the tread of Godzilla. I hear blood booming in my ears and gusts of my breath, hijacked by laughter.

Photo by Tania Powell

Acknowledgements

My father initiated Emily and I into the art of writing thank you letters when we were quite young. He said that the letter should be like the most delicious of recipes, where the star ingredient is enhanced by less integral yet vital ingredients. The *thank you* itself, he maintained, should come midway through the letter, between newsy anecdotes pertinent to the recipient, to make it as hearty as possible, and thereby acknowledging the precious thought that had gone (or not) into the gift. We were to draft every letter three times. The final copy, at least two sides in length, was written on plain paper, and our childish handwriting teetered across the lines just visible from a black felt-tipped template sheet beneath. Each letter took a couple of hours to perfect. This book has also taken a while (I feel the breeze of vigorous nodding), and there are many people to whom I'm indebted, and to whom I should write. Indeed, the volume of letters would amount to a book. In the meantime, I'm grateful for the opportunity to thank a few here.

Matt Winkler, and Nick Burfitt, and their teams, and all who cared for me at Charing Cross Hospital, Imperial College Healthcare NHS Trust: thank you for saving my life.

And thank you to Mr Mohammed and Joan, my bedside saviours. And to the phlebotomist who had the gentlest scratch.

For bringing *Gargoyles* to life: thank you to my agent Ivan Mulcahy for his perseverance, and for being there when it very much mattered. Thank you to the visionary and insightful

HARRIET MERCER

Nathan Connolly, editor at Dead Ink Books (and juggler extraordinaire) for his faith in me, and for understanding. Thank you, too, to the superstar Jordan Taylor-Jones; to Dan Coxon for his attention to detail, and to all who contribute to Dead Ink, the far from *scrappy* little press.

Thank you to Carrie Leyva for transforming my eccentric paragraphing and spacing into an elegant manuscript, and for her friendship. Thank you to George Koutroumanidis for his gargoyle illustration, and for his patience and humour on our wonderful walks while I ramble on, and on.

Thank you to Lisa Miller for her generosity in allowing me to tell her story. Thank you to Elizabeth Auriol Peers for permitting me to share her work. Thank you to my Camino Walk heroes, especially Kay's Crew, and Devin Smith. And thank you to the authors and filmmakers I've included, whose stories will continue to inspire me; in particular, Jean-Dominique Bauby; Sonali Deraniyagala; David Grossman; and Juliane Koepcke.

Thank you to my beloved writing group for their honesty, encouragement and most importantly, friendship: Sam Barlow; Arun Debnath; Emmett Fitzgerald; Hind Makiya; Paul Murphy; Jo Ooi; Sam Roddick; to Gillian Slovo for igniting it all, and, with an extra hug for hosting our retreats at her glorious home, Jasmin Tempest.

Deep gratitude to friends, teachers, and colleagues who have also been integral to my writing, whether they have read, inspired, or helped in ways they may not realise, especially: Kathy Allen; Jocelyn Bain Hogg; Richard Barrett; Jonathan Branson; Matthew Burrows; Mark Cheeseman; Susan Clarke; Katherine Freeland; Susanna Jones; Andy Lewis; Eley McAinsh; Bonnie McDonald; Don McGovern; Peter Miles; Andrew Motion, The Mulberry Centre Book Club; Greg Naysmith; Moe Moe Oo; Neal Sumner; Ariadne Van de Ven; Bill Vellutini; and Kate Williams.

Big love and special thanks to the following, whose friendship and encouragement have been my mainstay: Pete and Alice Burden; John Crook, Nell Crook, Gareth Furby; the Koutroumanidis family; Tania Powell; Lyn Rhodes; Minakshi Roy; Allen Samuels; Shenagh and Sheena; Melody Schroeder; Amelia SWEETIE Stewart; Gerry Summers; and Arthur Warsop.

I'm indebted to both our grandmothers, whose love of books infiltrated me from as soon as I could read, and to our Aunt Enid who was always so interested in my writing.

I am, as you have read, incredibly fortunate to have the family that I do, and I thank them with all my love: my loving, valiant mother, and my lion-hearted sister, Emily; Alice; Maddy; Simon and Max.

My father is probably looking down, urging me to get writing the thank you letters.

He will see me see looking up, and all around, wishing I could say, *thank you, Daddy*, in person.

Bibliography

Baldwin, James, *Giovanni's Room*. London: Penguin Books. 2007.

Barnes, Julian, *Levels of Life*. Great Britain: Jonathan Cape. 2013.

Bauby, Jean-Dominique, *The Diving-Bell and the Butterfly*. London: Fourth Estate. 1997.

Berger, John, *and our faces, my heart, brief as photos*. London: Bloomsbury Publishing. 2005.

Caruth, Cathy, *Unclaimed Experience*. USA: The John Hopkins University Press. 1996.

Courtenay, Tamsin, *Four Feet Under*. Great Britain: Unbound. 2018.

Daudet, Alphonse, *In the Land of Pain*. Translated by Julian Barnes. Great Britain: Jonathan Cape. 2002.

Deraniyagala, Sonali, *Wave*. Great Britain: Virago Press. 2013.

Didion, Joan, *The White Album*. New York: Farrar, Straus and Giroux. 1990.

Didion, Joan, *The Year of Magical Thinking*. Great Britain: Fourth Estate. 2012.

Donne, John, *Devotions upon Emergent Occasions and Death's Duel*. USA: Vintage. 1999.

Forster, E.M., *A Room with a View*. London: Penguin Books. 1986.

Grossman, David, *A Horse Walks into a Bar*. Translated by Jessica Cohen. Great Britain: Jonathan Cape. 2016.

Grossman, David, *To the End of the Land*. Translated by Jessica Cohen. Great Britain: Vintage. 2010.

Grossman, David, *Falling Out of Time*. Translated by Jessica Cohen. Great Britain: Jonathan Cape. 2014.

Hardy, Thomas, *Tess of the D'Urbervilles*. London: Macmillan And Co. 1927.

Homer, *The Odyssey*. Translated by Emily Wilson. New York: W.W. Norton & Company, Inc. 2018.

Kang, Han, *The Vegetarian*. London: Portobello Books. 2015.

Koepcke, Juliane, *When I Fell From The Sky*. London: Nicholas Brealey Publishing. 2012.

Louis, Édouard, *History of Violence*. London: Harvill Secker. 2018.

McBride, Eimar, *A Girl is a Half-Formed Thing*. Great Britain: Faber & Faber Limited and Galley Beggar Press. 2014.

Mantel, Hilary, *Giving Up the Ghost*. Great Britain: Fourth Estate. 2010.

Mantel, Hilary, 'Meeting the Devil.' In *Meeting the Devil*, edited by London Review of Books. London: William Heinemann. 2013.

Marvell, Andrew, *The Complete Poems*. London: Penguin Books. 2005

Oswald, Alice, *Falling Awake*. New York: W.W. Norton & Company, Inc. 2016.

Pamuk, Orhan, *The Museum of Innocence*. Translated by Maureen Freely. London: Faber & Faber Limited. 2009.

Scarry, Elaine, *The Body in Pain*. Great Britain: Oxford University Press. 1985.

Sontag, Susan, *Illness as a Metaphor & Aids and its Metaphors*. Great Britain: Penguin Classics. 1991.

Withycombe, Shannon, *Lost: Miscarriage in Nineteenth Century America*. USA: Rutgers University Press. 2018.

Woolf, Virginia, *On Being Ill*. USA: Paris Press. 2002.

Films

Gary Gulman: The Great Depresh. TV Movie. USA: HBO. 2019.

Joker. Directed by Todd Phillips. USA: Warner Bros. 2019.

Locked-in Syndrome. DVD. Directed by Jean-Jacques Beineix. France: Cargo Films. 1997.

The Cats of Mirikitani. DVD. Directed by Linda Hattendorf. USA: Lucid Dreaming Inc; Arthouse Films. 2006.

Toni Erdmann. Directed by Maren Ade. Austria and Germany: Komplizen Film. 2016.

About the Author

Harriet Mercer lives in Teddington, South West London. She received a distinction for her MA in Creative Writing at Royal Holloway and was awarded the University of London Creative Writing Prize. Harriet is rarely without her camera; a lover of nature and the arts, she is inspired to find beauty in the everyday, and everywhere.